Soccer Fit

SOCCER FIT

TRAINING & HEALTH FOR SOCCER PLAYERS

Mervyn Beck

The Crowood Press

First published in 1991 by
The Crowood Press Ltd
Gipsy Lane, Swindon
Wiltshire SN2 6DQ

British Library Cataloguing in Publication Data

Beck, Mervyn
    Soccer fit.
    1. Association football. Players. Physical fitness
    I. Title
    613.711

ISBN 1 85223 472 5

Acknowledgements

I should like to thank two of my colleagues for their help with
Chapter 1. Dr Ron Butterly for discussions regarding the
appropriateness of the material and Dr John Humphreys for
his comments on the content and accuracy of the first draft.
My thanks also go to Audrey Sykes, who typed the script, for
her patience and diligence in making all the necessary
corrections and minor additions to the content.
    Grateful acknowledgement is made to the Australian
Coaching Council for permission to reprint tabulated data
by Withers R.T. (1978) from their journal *Sports Coach*.
    I am grateful also to Brian Duffy and Andrew Thomas for
being such helpful subjects for the photographs in the book.

All photographs were taken by Brendan Corr.
All line-drawings are by Jan Sparrow.

Dedicated to Norma

Author's Note
This book is intended for male and female soccer players.
The masculine gender is used throughout merely to avoid
the continual appearance of he/she.

Typeset by Acūté, Stroud, Glos
Printed and bound in Great Britain by BPCC Hazell Books, Aylesbury

Contents

Introduction

This book is written with soccer players in mind. It attempts to explain the requirements of a fitness training programme and to give some ideas on ways of achieving fitness.

Many of the drills could be adapted and used by an individual who trains alone but it is recognized that with a team game such as soccer, it is normal and desirable to train with others. The practices and drills are therefore aimed at pairs, or small groups of players.

The book is also intended for the beginner coach or manager, in the hope that some of the information will give a sound basis for planning and for extending ideas for the future. It may also act as a reference for questioning current schedules of fitness training used by some coaches and managers, where methods have remained largely unchanged over time.

One simple principle should pervade all the drills and practices: the belief that the ball should be used wherever possible. This book does not claim to be revolutionary but the ideas for training are based upon known research and the stretching and flexibility exercises are suggested in the light of current thinking regarding the dangers of some previous exercises, which have featured in fitness training sessions down the years.

A few practices have been included for the very specialised training of goalkeepers. These cannot be exhaustive in a work of this size and further reading has been suggested. Other topics touched upon in a superficial way, such as injury rehabilitation and diet, have references for further reading in the bibliography.

It is hoped that the book will stimulate thought concerning why we do what we do, in soccer fitness training.

Symbols Used

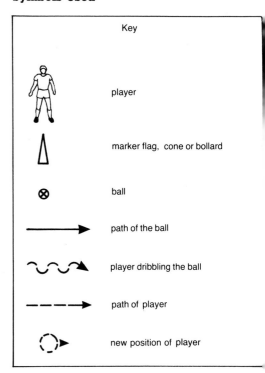

	Key
	player
	marker flag, cone or bollard
	ball
	path of the ball
	player dribbling the ball
	path of player
	new position of player

1 What Is Fitness?

Fitness, or physical work capacity, means different things to different people. The golfer who walks several miles in pursuit of his sport but who never runs will claim that he is fit. Similarly, the racing-car driver requires a high level of fitness and trains hard for his sport, even though he sits strapped inside the cockpit of his car during the entire event. The swimmer, the track sprinter, the shot putter and the marathon runner all have their particular kinds of fitness and the soccer player is just one more athlete who requires a very special form and level of fitness. Fitness is different for each sport or physical activity and a special training programme is associated with each particular sport. This is known as the specificity of training.

At a simple level of understanding fitness is the capacity of the human body to do work. The specific nature of fitness for each activity or sport, depends upon:

1   How much work is to be done.
2   How intense the workload is.
3   How long the work period lasts.
4   How much time is available for recovery between each period of work.

It can readily be appreciated that the 100-metre or 200-metre sprinter will require a special programme of preparation but that the energy output demands will last for only short periods of time. By comparison, the energy output demands made upon the soccer player will be vastly different, as he is required to sprint various distances during the 90 minutes of the game, with irregular rest periods in between each sprint. The level of fitness of each player will determine how often he can sprint and how long he will take to recover from each period of intense work.

TYPES OF FITNESS

A soccer player requires two main forms of fitness, aerobic and anaerobic. Anaerobic fitness involves two main systems, the ATP/PC system and the lactic acid (LA) system.

Aerobic Fitness

Aerobic fitness (sometimes called stamina or the oxygen system) is when the body uses oxygen from the air we breathe to combine with simple sugars in the muscles to create energy. This system can last for long periods of time and as long as the body can supply sugar (in the form of glycogen) to the working muscles and oxygen from the air, it can operate indefinitely. The necessary oxygen and glycogen are supplied to the working muscles via the blood and circulatory system.

The intensity of aerobic work during a game can vary from fast walking to jogging or striding; but generally it means that the heart rate is at least 150–170 beats per minute (BPM) and often higher. Most fully trained players can cope with these demands.

Anaerobic Fitness

This is when the body uses adenosine triphosphate/phosphocreatine (ATP/PC) and glycogen, which is stored in the muscle cells, for a sudden and explosive action such as sprinting. It is sometimes called the anaerobic system. It involves incurring an oxygen debt and therefore there is a limit to the length of time which a player can sustain this level of output. Eventually the muscle cannot function properly at such a high intensity of work, because of the build-up of waste products (such as lactic acid) within the cells of the muscle. A period of time is then needed during which the muscle replenishes its store of oxygen and glycogen. This 'rest period' can be looked upon as repaying the debt to the muscle fibres. The 'rest period' is a comparative term, since the player may have stopped sprinting but be engaged in jogging or striding. The level of work output, however, has decreased and although he is now operating at an aerobic level, the anaerobic system is being replenished.

Anaerobic fitness is often associated with how quickly the player can recover from one sprint and restart a further burst of speed. This time lag is dependent upon the efficiency of the bodily systems to recover from a phase of intense work and prepare the body for another spell of hard work.

The process takes time and involves the cardio-respiratory system (heart, lungs, blood and blood vessels) as well as the glycogen-supplying system from the liver. It will be readily appreciated that the bodily systems of each person will cope with the demands in a unique and individual way.

All high-intensity work involving sudden sprints and jumps is supplied with energy from this system. It lasts about 3–5 seconds as there are limits to the amount of ATP/PC which can be stored in a muscle. If a player wants to continue with high-intensity work he will need to produce more ATP and this is done via the other anaerobic system, namely the lactic acid (LA) system.

The Lactic Acid System

Like the ATP/PC system, the LA system produces limited amounts of energy (probably up to two minutes) but tries to continue to allow the player to work at high intensity. The lactic acid system depends upon the breakdown of glycogen within the muscles but, because the activity is high-intensity, there is an absence of oxygen and therefore ATP is produced in limited amounts. This ATP helps to replenish the ATP/PC system but if the

intensity of work persists, eventually there is a build-up of lactic acid within the muscle, which causes local muscle fatigue. Time is then required to disperse the lactic acid, but during this recovery period the player may operate at the aerobic level.

Here the efficiency of the player's bodily systems are put to the test as the muscles try to reproduce ATP in preparation for the next phase of high-intensity work. The time interval taken to prepare for the next burst of high energy output is often associated with how fit the player is.

In soccer, therefore, a player switches readily between the three energy systems outlined – the aerobic system and the two anaerobic systems – as he sprints, jogs, strides, walks and jumps during the game. The total amount of work that he achieves depends upon the efficiency of his body to produce energy at the appropriate level when required and to recover quickly, so that he is ready for another period of high-intensity work as soon as possible. This total output can be related to the player's level of fitness. The fitter the player, the more work he will be able to do because he will spend less time in the periods of recovery and rest.

WHERE DOES THE ENERGY COME FROM?

The energy from the breakdown of the food we eat is not the energy which is used for muscular activity. The energy from food is used to manufacture ATP, which is then supplied to and stored in the muscle cells. The energy subsequently released from the breakdown of ATP is what fuels muscular activity. The energy production processes are represented diagrammatically in Fig 1.

During exercise there is a linked system of energy use and production. First, energy is released from the breakdown of ATP in the muscles to supply energy for muscular work and movement; second, energy is produced

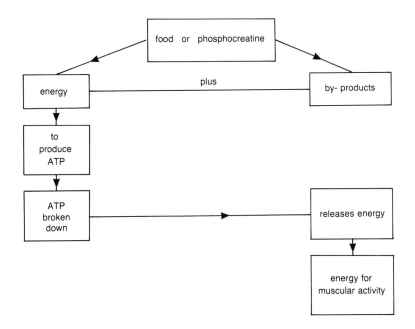

Fig 1   The energy production processes.

from food or phosphocreatine in order to replace the supply of ATP in the muscles. This is a simplified summary of what is a very complex series of chemical reactions. Fitness is determined by how efficiently the body supplies these energy needs as demanded by the soccer player.

HOW IS FITNESS MEASURED?

We have noted that fitness is the ability to do work and that this involves the production of energy. In order to produce energy, oxygen is consumed and this is provided either from the air (aerobic energy) or by the muscle in the form of stored oxygen. Fitness can therefore be related to how efficiently the body utilizes oxygen.

Aerobic Power Tests

A straightforward laboratory test for a player would be to run on a treadmill for a given length of time at a known speed. The air expired by the player is collected and analysed and this gives a measure of how much oxygen he has used. Other measures which are taken are heart rate, breathing rate, CO_2 content, ventilation rate per minute and body weight. From these readings it is possible to measure how efficiently the player has used oxygen and, in conjunction with tests to analyse the condition of the player's blood, provides a very good indication of the overall aerobic fitness of the player.

This test gives us a measure of maximum oxygen consumption and is associated with determining a person's maximal aerobic power. This is called the max $\dot{V}O_2$ value and is the most common method of measuring an athlete's heart and lung respiratory fitness. Max $\dot{V}O_2$ depends upon the age, sex, body size and composition of the individual and can be measured by means of a treadmill, a bicycle ergometer, or a bench-stepping technique.

Finding the true max $\dot{V}O_2$ value for a person is difficult and time-consuming and more

9

recently a simple method for predicting max $\dot{V}O_2$ in males has been described. It is based on an equation using the submaximal heart rate (HR sub.) recorded during the fifth minute of bicycle exercise at approximately 150 watts. The equation is:[1]

Predicted max $\dot{V}O_2$ in litres per minute = 6.3 $-$ (0.0193 × HR sub)

For example, if HR sub. is 160, predicted max $\dot{V}O_2$ = 6.3 – (0.0193 × 160), or 3.21 litres per minute. (If the subject is older than 25 years of age, the Åstrand–Åstrand age correction factor should be used.[2])

For the majority of people the maximum aerobic power is recorded around the ages of 15–17 and begins to decline around the age of 30. With soccer players, however, who would be amongst some of the fittest sports people, the higher readings would last well into the late twenties and decline only when the player stops serious training for the sport.

Average readings for men aged 20–30 years would be between 3.0 and 3.5 litres per minute or 41–48ml per kg per minute. For women this average would be between 2.0 and 2.5 litres per minute or 35 and 43ml per kg per minute. For fit sports people the expected readings would be in the range 50–60ml per kg per minute for women and 60–70 for men. (See Appendix I, Table A, for further information.)

This is the most straightforward test to ascertain aerobic power in soccer players. Compared with other methods it is fairly simple to administer and requires only a bicycle ergometer accurately calibrated to give a loading of 150 watts and accurate stop watches to measure the heart rate at the carotid artery. A full description is given in Appendix II.

Anaerobic Power Tests

Several tests can be used to give a measure of anaerobic power, including the Sargent jump and the Magaria-Kalamen power test, both of which are recorded by Fox and Mathews[3], along with their strengths and weaknesses as measures and associated reference tables. The test which could readily be used for soccer players because of its simplicity, is the Kalamen 50-yard dash. This involves an accurate measure of the time taken to sprint 50 yards from a 15-yard running start. For total accuracy the test should involve breaking a light beam at the start and finish of the dash. The results from this test compare very favourably with the most accurate measure of anaerobic power, namely the Magaria-Kalamen power test.

A simplified form of the 50-yard dash is given in Appendix III but it must be remembered that the value of the readings depends on the level of accuracy achieved in the timing of the test.

Readings for fit players would be in the following ranges:[4]

Women	15–20 years, under 7.9 seconds
	20–30 years, under 8.7 seconds
Men	15–20 years, under 6.5 seconds
	20–30 years, under 7.1 seconds

SUMMARY

A soccer player requires two main forms of fitness for his sport. First he must have a good cardio-respiratory endurance (aerobic) base to his fitness; second, he needs explosive (anaerobic) power for the sudden sprints and jumps which are demanded in the game. Fairly simple methods of assessing these two forms of fitness have been suggested, along with the apparatus required. The value of such tests as a comparative form of assessment for a squad of players depends on the accuracy with which the tests can be carried out. Generally speaking, fitness is associated with how quickly a player can recover from a burst of high-intensity work and the maximum amount of oxygen he can consume during sustained periods of exercise.

2 Getting Fit

In this chapter we shall consider the relationship between fitness and skill and the elements which are included in a discussion of fitness.

FITNESS AND SKILL

Soccer is a game involving skill, in which the techniques are used to carry out the decisions which are made. Skill comprises several components, as shown in Fig 2.

Fitness is a vital component of soccer skill. A player has to make decisions relating to the game during every second and in order to do this he has to be fit. When fatigue sets in a player can become sluggish in his movements and his technique will deteriorate. His speed, strength, power and stamina are all affected and the quality of his play will diminish. Mentally he may try to drive himself to greater efforts and this can assist in delaying the effects of fatigue, but eventually his tiredness will affect his mental alertness and to the observer it will be obvious that the player is tired and that the quality of his play has deteriorated.

We know that all players become tired eventually but high levels of fitness can delay the onset of fatigue and this can keep the skill level high for longer periods of time. Fitness affects skill in the following ways:

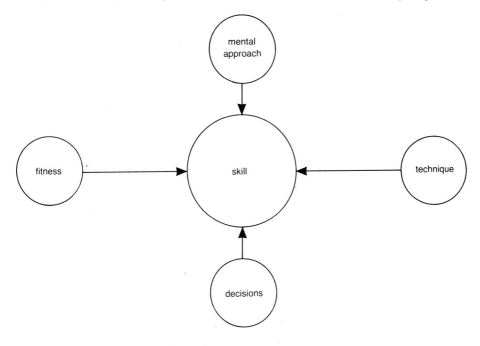

Fig 2   The components of skill.

1   It allows the player to use the elements of speed, strength, power, stamina and flexibility to good effect in carrying out the techniques of the game.
2   It allows the player to maintain the quality of his performance for longer periods of time.
3   It keeps the player mentally alert, especially in the last quarter of the game.
4   Mental alertness will aid the player in making decisions during the game, especially in the latter stages. This is a very important aspect of skill and involves the player in deciding when and how to apply a technique.

Fitness determines to a large extent the level of skill which a player can display. As fatigue sets in, skilfulness begins to deteriorate and the player is seen to make an increasing number of errors in his play.

All sports people know that if they wish to function at a high level of performance they will have to train hard. At some stage this will hurt and unless a player has the correct attitude towards training he will generally settle for efforts which are below his maximum. Let us assume, however, that the player is highly motivated and look at a programme which is designed to get him fit.

THE ELEMENTS OF FITNESS

Fitness is made up of several elements, as shown in Fig 3. A training programme will include the following.

1   Speed – sprinting various distances at maximum speed (anaerobic work).
2   Stamina – work which is not at maximum speed but involves jogging, striding, and walking (aerobic work).
3   Strength – involving muscles working against a resistance.
4   Flexibility – exercises which stretch muscles and tendons and mobilize joints.

WHAT DOES THE GAME DEMAND?

At first one might assume that the game demands that you work vigorously for 90

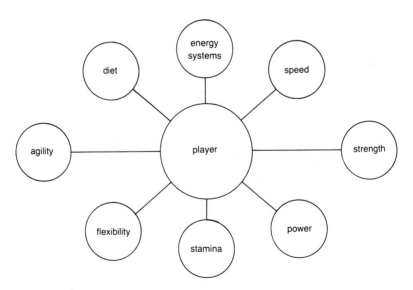

Fig 3   The elements of fitness.

minutes but a closer look shows that this is not necessarily the case. The ball may be out of play for anything between 15 and 30 minutes of the entire match and during these periods the player can be considered to be at rest. For the remainder of the game, the player is involved in a work rate which is dependent upon his playing position.

Fitness for soccer therefore involves an analysis of the requirements of the game and then devising a programme of training which will meet the demands of each playing position. This varies considerably within a team and it can readily be appreciated that the demands made upon the goalkeeper are very different from those made upon a centre back, a midfield player, or a centre forward.

Research over the past forty years has centred mainly on two aspects of soccer playing. First there has been considerable analysis of distances covered by players during a game. Second, more scientific methods

have allowed the individual levels of fitness of each player in a team to be monitored. These two areas of research have implications for the preparation of soccer players.

Distances Covered in a Soccer Match

The findings regarding work done by players show wide variation and the results, shown in the table, are helpful in providing an average figure or guide for training purposes. This knowledge has assisted in determining the structure of training schedules. For example, if the average figure for the distance sprinted in a game is adopted and we also know that this is made up of sprints over distances of about 15–25 metres, this can be reflected in the training schedule. Each manager or coach can construct his own training programme based upon the total demand for sprints and overall distances to be covered.

Author and Date	**Walk**	**Jog**	**Sprint**	**Other**	**Total**
Winterbottom, 1959[vii]	–	2347	1014	–	3361
Wade, 1967[v]	–	1500–4000	250–2000	–	1750–6000
Zelenka, 1967[ix]	–	–	–	–	11500
Vinnai, 1973[iv]	–	–	–	–	17000
Saltin, 1973[iii]	3250	–	2880	5880	12010
Reilly and Thomas, 1976[ii]	2150	3187	974	2369	8680
Whitehead, 1968[vi]	–	2025	1748	7919	11692
Withers, 1978[viii]	3026	5139	666	2696	11527
Ekbolm, 1986[i]	–	–	800	9200	10000

Distances covered by soccer players in metres (average readings in most cases).[17]

Leaving out the readings from Zelenka and Vinnai, the averages of the various distances given in the table above are as follows.

Walk	Jog	Sprint	Other	Total
2653	3534	1579	4740	12506

(Appendices IV – VI provide further analysis by playing position.)

The data could be brought up to date with more recent information but the point is that a training schedule can be based on sound evidence. Each coach or manager can check the distances covered by the busiest players by means of video and paper-and-pencil methods (see Appendices VII and VIII).

Laboratory Research

Laboratory methods have improved enormously during the last fifteen years and players can now be tested on a wide range of parameters, which give a clear indication of present levels of fitness and can also help in predicting possible future potential.

Max $\dot{V}O_2$

First the measure of max $\dot{V}O_2$ tells us how efficient a player's body is in utilizing oxygen. It will tell us something about his maximum lung capacity and, coupled with blood tests to ascertain the haemoglobin levels in the blood stream, it can give a good indication of whether or not the player could withstand the rigorous demands of midfield play.

Second, we can investigate the proportions of fast-twitch and slow-twitch fibres in a muscle by muscle biopsy and therefore reach decisions on the desirability of further speed training for certain players. It is known that speed is associated with the proportions of fast- and slow-twitch fibres in the make-up of an athlete's muscles and this knowledge, added to other information on measures for heart and lung efficiency and max $\dot{V}O_2$, can

give a good picture of a player's current state of fitness and some ideas on which to base future training emphasis.[5])

For example, if it is suggested that a player needs speed training but it is known that he has a low ratio of fast-twitch fibres in his muscles, then it may be more beneficial to concentrate on his stamina training and ball technique than to spend time trying to improve his speed. Knowledge such as this can be used in constructing schedules of training which take account of the individual profiles of players. It could show that it may be wiser to work on a player's strengths rather than spend time on his weaknesses. If, for instance, it is thought that a player has reached a ceiling in terms of speed it may be more advantageous to work on his change of speed over short distances and concentrate on ball touch and game techniques, rather than persevere with speed training.

Most managers and coaches are aware of these factors at a common-sense level, but research and scientific analysis can also help in reaching sound decisions regarding a player. Surprisingly, clubs involved in the transfer of players, where vast sums of money are exchanged, still do not seek knowledge of a scientific kind to inform them of a player's current fitness and physiological potential.

Most club training schedules, however, are based on 'handed down' information and each coach or manager, follows the methods and procedures he himself has experienced. Most certainly the many courses at local and national level organized by the Football Association (FA) and the National Coaching Foundation (NFC) have contributed significantly to the thinking behind the training programmes in soccer and during the past twenty years fitness training has had a more scientific approach at all levels of the game.

Where possible it is appropriate to construct training schedules which take into account the specific playing position of the player, so that particular aspects of his functional requirements can be met. A simple example of this would be for a centre back, who moves 10 metres to jump to head a ball and as soon as he lands sprints 25 metres before a recovery phase. This takes into account the need for a centre back to practise heading, jumping and sprinting short distances.

CONSTRUCTING A TRAINING SCHEDULE

The walking, jogging, and other movement distances will be covered in a training session by the warm-up, related practices and any final games. What is being considered here is the important element of sprinting.

Most of the sprinting done by the soccer player is over distances between 10 and 35 metres. Runs to support players on the ball and recovery runs after an attack has broken down often exceed 50 metres. For example, the recovering full back, after an attacking overlap, may be expected to sprint up to 110 metres, but the proportion of these longer sprints is small compared with the bulk of the player's work, which takes place between 10 and 50 metres.

A suggested sprint requirement in a game would generally comprise:

10–30 metres	40 per cent
30–50 metres	40 per cent
50 metres plus	20 per cent

The training schedule for sprinting could then be constructed as follows:

Target distance 1500 metres

Sprinting 10–30 metres	600 metres
Sprinting 30–50 metres	600 metres
Sprinting 50 metres plus	300 metres
Total	1,500 metres

SPRINT DRILLS

We will turn now to consider some drills which can be used for achieving the sprint requirements of training. They are divided into practices with and without a ball.

With a Ball

Drill 1

Player X starts in the middle of two bollards (A and B) placed 10 metres apart. He sprints round the bollard at A. As he passes the mid-

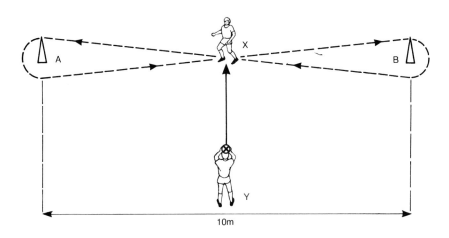

Fig 4   Drill 1.

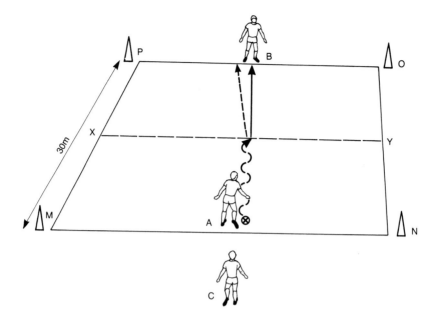

Fig 5   Drill 2.

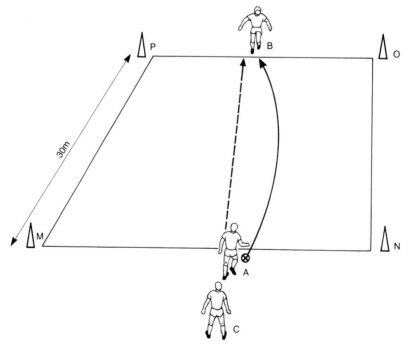

Fig 6   Drill 3.

point between A and B player Y passes the ball to him and he has to return it with one touch to player Y. He then sprints round bollard B.

This is repeated two times to each bollard.

    Distance sprinted = 40 metres
    Repetitions × 5   = 200 metres
    Work ratio 1:1

NOTE   The service is from hands and can be varied so that the performing player has to return the ball with his foot, knee, thigh, chest, or head.

Drill 2

Player A dribbles the ball to the mid-line XY where he passes the ball to B and then sprints to the end line. B now repeats the drill on the way back to player C. Player C repeats the drill to end line to player A. And so on.

    Distance sprinted = 15 metres
    Repetitions × 10   = 150 metres
    Work ratio 1:2

Drill 3

Player A chips the ball to B and sprints to line OP. B now chips the ball to C and sprints to line MN. Player C chips the ball to A and sprints to line OP. And so on.

    Distance sprinted = 30 metres
    Repetitions × 10   = 300 metres
    Work ratio 1:2

NOTE   This drill can be done with lobbed, driven or swerved passes before the player sprints.

Drill 4   50-Metres Straight Run

Play the ball to the other group of players and sprint – A to D, D to B, and so on.

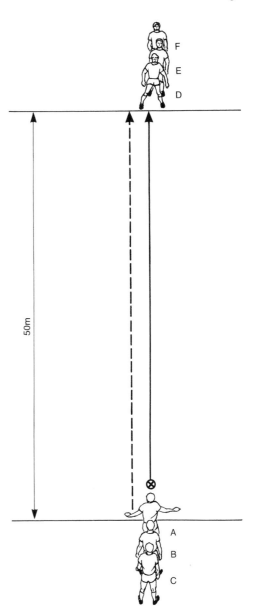

Fig 7   Drill 4.

    Distance sprinted = 50 metres
    Repetitions × 10   = 500 metres
    Work ratio 1:6

17

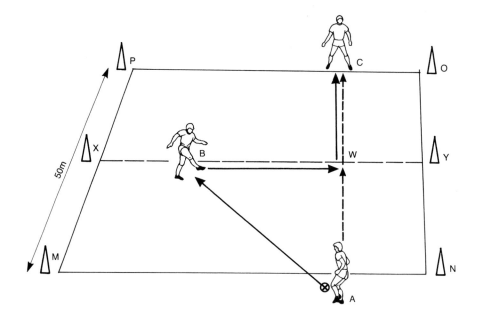

Fig 8   Drill 5.

Drill 5

Player A lofts the ball to B and sprints to point W on line XY. He receives a return pass from player B and immediately passes the ball to player C and sprints to position of C on line OP. Player B now jogs to position A on MN and player C dribbles the ball to position B on XY. Finally, player C passes the ball to player B, who is now at A, and the drill starts again.

NOTE   This is a two-stage sprint where the performing player has to check his speed for the return pass on line XY. The practice should eventually be done using one touch only for each player at A and B and W.

Distance sprinted   = 50 metres
Repetitions × 10   = 500 metres
Work ratio 1:2

Drill 6

Players A and B start off at the same time. Player A dribbles the ball to point W on XY.

At this point player A puts his foot on the ball to stop it. Player B takes the ball and accelerates to end line MN. Player A now sprints to line OP. Players C and D and E and F now repeat the drill.

NOTE   Look for acceleration after the change-over of the ball at W.

Distance sprinted   = 25 metres
Repetitions × 10   = 250 metres
Work ratio 1:2

Drill 7   Squares Sprinting

Player A runs round the square (once or twice). Players B, C and D have to pass the ball around the two sides of the square DC and CB three times (or six times) before A completes the square(s). Repeat for players B, C and D.

Sprint one square   = 80 metres
Sprint two squares = 160 metres
(Squares can be of different dimensions)
Work ratio 1:3

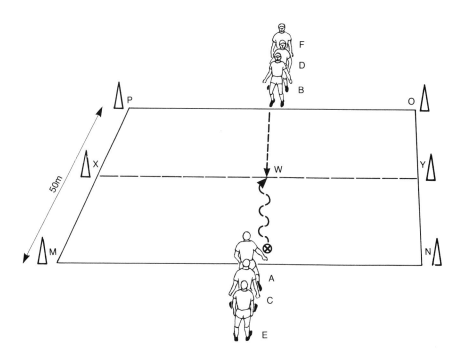

Fig 9   Drill 6.

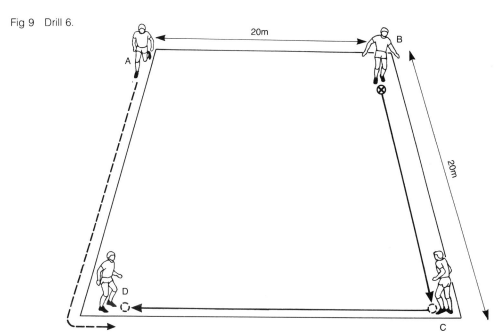

Fig 10   Drill 7.

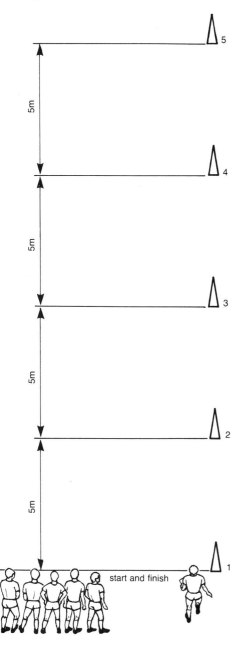

Fig 11   Drill 8.

Without a Ball

Drill 8 Shuttle Runs

Touch the ground beyond each bollard (1–5) in turn and return to the starting line. Emphasize the push-off as the player changes direction. This puts an overload on his leg muscles and the ankle and knee joints.

    Total distance = 100 metres
    Work ratio 1:5

Drill 9 Kite Run

Run to each bollard (A,B and C) and back. Touch the ground beyond the bollard. Run backwards when returning from bollards A and C.

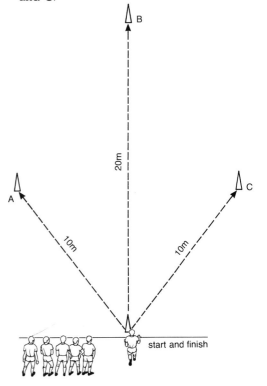

Fig 12   Drill 9.

Total distance = 80 metres
Work ratio 1:5

Drill 10 Full-Pitch Fartlek

Players begin at stations A, B, C, D, E and F.
There are four players (two pairs) at station A
and two players at each of the other stations.
Players run in pairs as follows:

First pair at A sprint to station B and then
jog to station C. As the players arrive at
station B the pair at B sprint to station C and
then jog to station D. The pair at C sprint to
station D and jog to station E. And so on.

One complete circuit = 175 metres sprint
                        175 metres jogging

Work ratio (sprint) 1:6

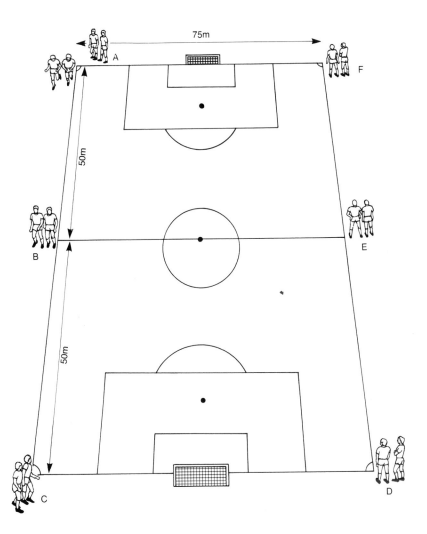

Fig 13   Drill 10.

3 Staying Fit

PERIODIZATION

Training schedules are planned for a whole year. Depending on the level of competition and the number of fixtures to be played by the club, the programme is constructed round two main considerations: the preparations for the first game and the preparations for each subsequent game.

THE PERIODS OF A SEASON

A typical Football League or non-league programme is made up of a pre-season period of six weeks, a playing season of thirty-eight weeks and a close season of eight weeks.

Pre-Season (Six Weeks)

The pre-season preparation is a very important period, since players will return in varying states of physical and mental condition. Some will be overweight and still mentally tuned to the vacation, whilst others will be quite fit and in good condition, both physically and mentally. Training should thus be planned with care, to avoid the common-denominator approach, which carries the risk of causing stress for some players. It may be preferable to select specific groups for slightly different training schedules rather than attempt too much too soon. Early sessions which are physically demanding risk injury to players. It is better to start off at an easy pace and accelerate the training as the season approaches. An injury during pre-season programmes can take a player well beyond the start of the season before he is fit to compete and this should be a serious consideration in the preparation of training schedules. There are in-juries during matches which are outside the control of managers and coaches but there are also injuries caused by stress-related physical considerations such as overtraining, and these can be avoided by careful thought, knowledge and planning.

In preparing pre-season programmes a coach should consider the following elements:

1 The physiological state of the player. His weight should be checked against his finishing weight of the previous season if possible. Resting pulse rate and heart rate after a 5-minute aerobic run could also be taken.
2 Emphasize aerobic training in the early stages. Heart rate during this work should be around 150–160 BPM for a training effect.
3 Incorporate ball work in all training where possible. This adds interest and develops technique and skills.
4 Increase anaerobic work as the pre-season period develops, building steadily towards the final week of preparation.
5 Note the levels of self-motivation on the part of the players.
6 Note any minor stresses and strains during training. Be ready to reduce the training load to assist with physical rehabilitation.

The following programme for pre-season training is based on two sessions each week for six weeks.

Week 1   *MINUTES*

Warm-up: ball touch exercises	20–30
Stretching exercises: all main joints and associated muscles	10–20
Continuous jog in positional groups	5
Recovery: ball work in small groups	10

Speed work: 10 × 50 metres (ratio 3:1), striding – no sprinting	10
Recovery: ball work	10
Continuous jog	5
Recovery: ball work	10
Small-sided games	20
Continuous jog	5
Stretching and slow jog	10
Total	115–135

Week 2

Warm-up: ball touch exercises	20–30
Stretching exercises	10–20
Continuous jog in positional groups	5
Recovery: ball work in small groups	10
Speed work: 5 × 50 metres striding and 5 × 50 metres extended stride	10
Recovery: ball work	10
Speed work: 300 metres (6 × 50); build up to nine-tenths of full speed	5
Recovery: ball work	10
Positional and technique work	20
Continuous jog	5
Stretching and slow jog	10
Total	115–135

Week 3

Warm-up: ball touch work	20–30
Stretching exercises	10–20
Continuous jog – increasing to striding	5
Recovery: ball work	10
Speed work: 500 metres (5 × 50 striding and 5 × 50 at nine-tenths full speed)	10
Recovery: ball work	10
Speedwork: 400 metres (8 × 50 metres full speed)	10
Game: coaching and principles of play	20

Power work – partner work	5
Continuous jog, increasing to striding	5
Stretching and slow jog	10
Total	115–135

Week 4

Warm-up: ball touch exercises	20–30
Stretching exercises	10–20
Continuous jog, increasing to striding	5
Recovery: ball work	5
Speed work: 750 metres (250 metres striding and 500 metres full sprint; work in distances of 25, 50 or 100 metres)	20
Recovery: ball work	10
Speed work: 750 metres (work in distances of 25 or 50 metres) full sprint	20
Game coaching	30
Stretching and slow jog	10
Total	130–150

Week 5

Warm-up: ball touch exercises	20–30
Stretching exercises	10–20
Continuous jog, increasing to striding	5
Recovery: ball work	5
Speed work: 750 metres (work in distances of 50, 100 and 150 metres) full sprint	25
Recovery: ball work	10
Speed work: 750 metres (work in distances of 25, 50 100 metres) full sprint	25
Game coaching	30
Power work	5
Stretching and slow jog	10
Total	145–165

Week 6

Warm-up: ball touch exercises	20–30

Stretching exercises	10–20
Continuous jog, increasing to striding	5
Recovery: ball work	10
Speed work: 750 metres (5 × 110 metres and 10 × 25 metres) full sprint	20
Recovery: ball work	10
Speed work: 750 metres (5 × 80 metres and 14 × 25 metres) full sprint	20
Recovery: ball work	10
Game coaching	30
Stretching and slow jog	10
Total	145–165

The Playing Season (Thirty-Eight Weeks)

If the training has been well structured and sensitively administered, players should arrive at the first game in good condition. There should be little excuse for a player who does not reach optimum fitness in the game of soccer today, since ample information is available in the literature and coaching courses. Ultimately it will be the confidence of the player himself that will govern his performance. If the physiological preparation has been adequate and sound, performance level will hinge upon the player's mental attitude.

There is little doubt that the playing season, with all its matches, helps to harden a player to the knocks and stresses of the game and has its own built-in training effect. Fitness during the season will fluctuate according to the individual player and the demands made upon him by the game schedule, his playing position and the club's training programme.

A player's fitness does not suddenly plummet downwards if he does not train for one or two weeks. The effects are gradual. What does seem certain is that there is a loss of muscle tone during any lay-off period. Generally a player can participate in light training during the recovery from bruises and strains but a more serious injury will need a careful and graded recovery period under the watchful eye of an experienced physiotherapist or doctor. After any period of inactivity a player will need to pay particular attention to the warm-up and the stretching exercises, prior to any work with a ball. Training then needs to be graded and progressive as the player applies more pressure and demand upon his muscles and joints. Rehabilitation from injury is a very specific and specialized area of soccer and cannot be covered adequately in this book. For further information on this subject, see the Bibliography.

Generally the recovery for any knee, hip, ankle, or other joint injury follows the sequence:

1 Move only in straight lines.
2 Move gradually into easy curves, tightening the curves as recovery progresses.
3 Move gradually to changing direction suddenly and with power on the turn.

Recovery from muscle bruising, strains and pulled fibres involves:

1 Specialist diagnosis of the problem.
2 A rehabilitation programme.
3 Specialist help with any massage, heat treatment or short-wave therapy.
4 Careful, prolonged warming-up sessions when beginning to use the muscle again.
5 Careful attention to the stretching exercises making sure there is no pain or discomfort.
6 Patience and the knowledge that nature will heal the problem if you allow time and do not hinder the process of recovery.

Closed Season (Eight Weeks)

Few players are totally inactive during this period and so fitness levels do not suddenly plummet to depths of chronic proportions. In the exceptional cases of total inactivity (which one can hardly begrudge a soccer player, if one considers the demands of the other 44 weeks) some of the factors involved could be:

1 A loss of muscle tone.
2 An increase in body fat levels.
3 A percentage deterioration in cardio-respiratory functioning.
4 Lowering of max $\dot{V}O_2$ values.

All these factors must be carefully considered when the player returns for pre-season training, which points to the need for careful monitoring of the physical condition of players at certain points in the training year. Total loss of fitness, however, is a rare occurrence, because most soccer players will be involved in some form of physical exercise during the eight-week holiday period. Swimming, tennis and walking often feature in the holiday recreation programme and each activity will make a contribution to the maintenance of a certain level of fitness. In simple terms, any physical activity will slow down the process of deterioration in fitness levels.

Research[6] shows that brief periods of inactivity can significantly decrease the performance of top-class athletes. Periods of 4 – 8 weeks of inactivity can reduce fitness to pre-training levels and therefore it seems safe to say that any activity which the player engages in during the holiday period will be of benefit when he returns for pre-season preparations. If a positive target could be set for the close season, then it would be advantageous if a player could jog about 3 miles and sprint 10 × 50 metres or its equivalent twice each week. This would give considerable benefits for aerobic and anaerobic components of fitness when pre-season training begins.

MAINTENANCE OF FITNESS

Maintaining fitness depends upon several factors, the main one being the match schedule for each week of the season. At both league and non-league level it is normal to train for fitness twice each week when the matches are only on a Saturday. From a fitness point of view two sessions should be sufficient, but where clubs are involved in mid-week fixtures a single hard training session should suffice. It is as important for the body to recover from the effects of training, or a match, as it is to work hard during the training session. Minor damage to muscle fibres, ligaments, tendons and blood vessels needs to be repaired. Bruising within a muscle or a joint needs time to disperse damaged blood cells and to remove excess fluids (swelling). Time is the factor here and the body can be helped in its recovery by expert treatment such as physiotherapy. It is worth noting that nature can also be hindered in the recovery phase and it is therefore essential to make sure that a player is receiving treatment from a well qualified professional and not an enthusiastic amateur.

Particular dangers exist for players who play in matches on successive days. This should receive special attention when teams are involved in tournaments, where, because of costs, the appropriate time lapse between each game cannot be considered.

There is little doubt that players run the risk of injury when they are required to play two games on successive days. Where this is absolutely necessary, it is very important to 'warm down' after the first and subsequent games. It is very worth while to spend 20–25 minutes in light jogging, stretching and mobilizing all the main muscles and joints. This will help to disperse waste products and fluid from the muscles and joint complexes as a result of a gentle squeezing and pumping from muscular activity. This activity avoids the retention of unwanted fluids which can be the cause of muscle or joint soreness and stiffness on the day following a match.

OVERTRAINING

All sports people know the effect of physical or psychological tiredness. During the long playing season for a soccer club players are often very jaded as they approach the final month of fixtures. A lot depends upon the motivation levels which the fixtures generate. If promotion or relegation issues still remain to be resolved the chances are that the players will be easily motivated, but where the outcome of the final games are of no consequence, the only true motivating factor is the pride of the individual player in his own performance – an important part of a player's personality. The willingness to give of one's best at all times is a priceless component in the profile of any player.

Then there is also the physical demand made by the schedule of matches which have to be played within the deadline of dates for the league. This dilemma particularly concerns teams which have done well in cup competitions, or have been involved in several replay matches. It is not uncommon for players to be asked to play on Saturday, Monday, Thursday and again on Saturday. Towards the end of a soccer season this is unrealistic, especially as the players will be expected to perform to a high level in each of the four games. Schedules worse than this are not unknown and fall into the category of overtraining. The effects upon the body and subsequent performance are as follows:

1   The body needs time to repair minor damage to muscle fibres, bruising to muscles, ruptures to small blood vessels and stresses and strains to joint ligaments and tendon insertions. This rest period, with only light exercises to aid healing, is as important as the training expected of the player.

2   After vigorous and exhausting exercise the replenishment of glycogen in the muscles will take up to 46 hours, and in the liver between 12 and 24 hours.[7]

3   Where glycogen replacement is not complete, performance will obviously deteriorate. The explosive power output from anaerobic energy sources will be reduced and a player will not seem to have any sharpness or alertness in his game.

4   Minor damage to muscles, tendons, ligaments and joints not repaired during periods of rest could be further damaged by overtraining, and lead to a more serious injury.

Overtraining effects are not confined to the end-of-season problems of fixture congestion. Overzealous coaches and managers can often overstep the limits of players' physical resources during pre-season training, where the efforts to make progress quickly in training sessions are punctuated with pre-season friendly matches. This often leads to injuries which could have been avoided but the player is forced to miss the beginning of the season because of the time needed for recovery.

The effects of overtraining are demonstrated by the pre-season schedule followed by a First Division Football League club which was carefully documented. When the players arrived at the first game of the new season they were physically and mentally exhausted. The result was that they were soundly beaten. This example is mentioned not to prove a point but to show that even at the top level in this country there is still room for an open-minded, reasoned and more scientific approach to training.

A former professional soccer player with First Division experience also looked into this topic for his undergraduate dissertation study.[8] Although there is a clear need to define what overtraining actually is, he found that players and coaches/managers understand the symptoms associated with the condition and that it leads to a drop in performance.

While solution to the problem involves many different factors, it does seem safe to state that between each Saturday, players should not be involved in more than one match, or two hard training sessions. The rest period between hard training sessions or matches should be seen as a serious part of total game preparation. Finally, light exercises, especially stretching, mobilizing and easy aerobic work, will aid in the recovery phase after a hard match or vigorous training.

4 Fitness Training Sessions

When the main aim of a session is fitness training, the general pattern is the following.

1 A thorough warm up.
2 Stretching and flexibility exercises.
3 Work involving striding and changes of speed.
4 Sprint work (maximum speed).
5 Related practices, techniques, skills, games.
6 Warming down, jogging, stretching.

GENERAL GUIDELINES

1 A gradual warm-up is essential and should lead into a graded stretching session. Players should be encouraged not to involve themselves in vigorous power demands from muscles (as in shooting) when they first arrive on the training ground.
2 Stretching exercises should involve static stretching rather than dynamic stretching.
3 In speed work players should ultimately work within a ratio of 5:1 (groups of six, with one working and five resting). This is based upon the notion that a player needs five times his exercise time for recovery purposes. However, in order to train for speed and endurance combined – for example, for midfield-players, it will be necessary to work players near to top speed with short rests in between each period of work. For this type of training (for the LA and O_2 systems combined) it will be necessary to work with ratios of 3:1 or even 2:1, so that heart rate is kept above 160 BPM for sustained periods of time. Some recent research[9] shows that heart rate during a professional game did not fall below 160 BPM for long periods and was near to 180 BPM on several occasions.

4 Speed work should follow the warm-up and stretching exercises. It should not follow the strength or power work (for example, any weight-training exercises).
5 The hard speed work should not take much more than 35 minutes and can be broken up with ball work.
6 Strength-training exercises using weights should be supervised. Expert advice should be sought where necessary for the correct exercise techniques, the appropriate weights and the repetitions to be used. Where unsure, use a light weight and increase the number of repetitions. Heavy weights, involving slow, powerful movements with large muscles, are not appropriate for soccer players.
7 Where players are involved in jogging on roads or hard surfaces, it is essential to wear the correct shock-absorbent training/jogging footwear. Generally speaking, this kind of training for soccer players is not recommended, since aerobic training can be achieved in other ways. Long cross-country runs will naturally aid aerobic fitness but time may be better utilized with ball practices and the use of 5 or 10-minute runs.
8 If a training session takes about 1–1½ hours and is well planned, it will approximate in demand to an actual game if the levels of activity are maintained.
9 The aerobic (stamina) work should not present a problem within the time available, so long as intensities of work rate are not allowed to drop too low.
10 To check work-rate levels, especially in the aerobic category, it is helpful and very informative occasionally to watch one player for ten minutes. Even under the watchful eye of a manager or coach, it is surprising how often a player stands still or walks during game-related practices.

Fig 14   Serve the ball to your partner underhand. Partner returns the ball with one touch using alternate feet.

Fig 15   Volley touch. Return the ball from thigh or knee.

28

IDEAS FOR WARM-UP

All warm-up work is done with a ball. This is because it is firmly believed that technique can be improved during sessions which focus on fitness. Too often the ball is omitted from fitness work and players lose an opportunity to touch a ball many times during the training session.

Drill 11   Volley Touch on the Spot

The following practices are all done whilst one person is running on the spot continuously for one minute. Work in pairs, with one ball between two people. Stand about 4 metres apart.

1   Serve the ball underhand. Keep a good rhythm. Partner returns the ball with a volley touch with alternate feet. The server catches the return (Fig 14).
2   Return the ball from thigh or knee (Fig 15).
3   Return the ball from the chest (Fig 16)
4   Return the ball from the head. Serve just above partner's head. Make him jump to head (Fig 17).

Drill 12   Volley Touch on the Move

For this drill, work again in pairs, moving backwards and forwards across the width of the field, one ball between two. Make sure the distance between pairs is kept to about

Fig 16   Volley touch. Return the ball from the chest.

Fig 17   Volley touch. Return the ball from the head.

4–5 metres. Emphasize good, light, springy footwork, with one person moving backwards, and the other person moving forwards. Bear in mind the following aspects as you practise this volley touch.

1   One-touch play from feet to partner. Partner, moving backwards, simply stops the ball, leaving it ready for the player moving forwards to play again. Change over roles on the way back across the field (Fig 18).

2   Serve from hands. Partner volley touches ball back whilst on the move (alternate feet). Partner catches the return (Fig 14.)

3   Serve from hands. Partner jumps to return ball from the chest. Partner catches the return (Fig 19).

4   Serve from hands. Partner returns ball from thigh or knee. Partner catches the return as in Fig 15.

5   Serve from hands just above partner's head. Partner jumps to head ball back. Partner catches the return. (The actions are as shown in Figs 14–17, except that the players are on the move.)

Progression

In the drills 11 and 12 above, the challenge can be stepped up by asking for a four-count rhythm for each of the practices: Player A serves to player B. Player B returns the ball to A. A then returns the ball to B using a similar volley touch (with his foot, thigh, chest or head) and then B finally returns the ball to A. A catches it and the drill begins again. This can be done either on the spot or on the move.

Fig 18   One-touch play from feet to partner.

Fig 19   Partner jumps to return the ball from the chest.

Drill 13   Pass and Rotate

All players move towards the line OP. Player A passes to D and then runs round his group to be behind player F. Player D now passes to B and then runs round his group to be behind player C, and so on. At the line OP the drill is reversed and players return to line MN. The distance between the two groups and the speed of movement may be varied.

Drill 14   Random Volley Touch Returns

Work in pairs, with one ball between two players. Work over the whole pitch but be aware of other players around you. Collisions must be avoided.

Both players move freely around the space. A serves a high ball to B (from hands or feet), making him move off the spot. B must get the

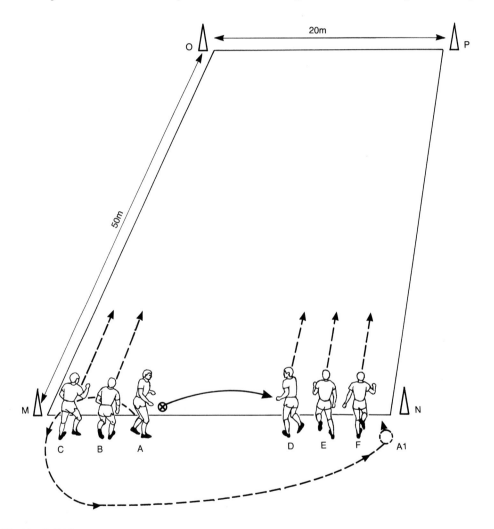

Fig 20   Drill 13.

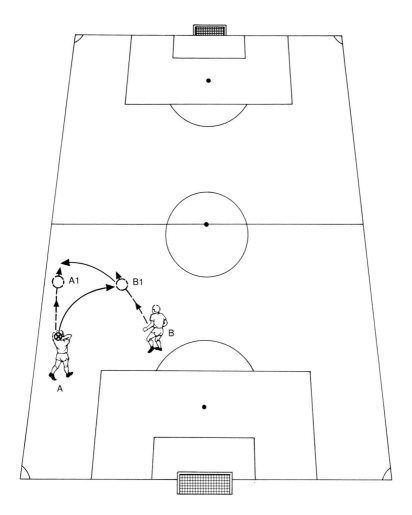

Fig 21   Drill 14.

ball back to A with one volley touch. The idea in this practice is to make your partner move as far as possible whilst the ball is in the air. If he cannot quite get there in time he must return the ball with one touch after it bounces. Returns can of course be from foot, head, thigh or knee. Change over after six serves.

Progression

A four-count rhythm can be asked of good players as follows:

A serves to B (from hands or feet).
B returns the ball with a volley touch to A.
A then returns the ball to B with a volley touch.
B returns the ball to A with a volley touch, and so on.

As players get better and better, see how many volley touches can be made before the practice breaks down.

NOTE   A good first serve will be high enough and far enough from the partner to make him move very quickly over 10–15 metres.

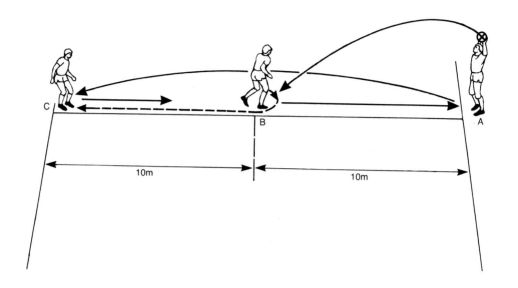

Fig 22   Drill 15.

Drill 15   Throw-In Drill

Three players, one ball.

A takes a throw-in to B. B volley-touches the ball back to A and turns to run to position C. A plays the ball to C. C gives a pass to B as he moves towards C. B returns the ball to C who now dribbles with the ball to position A. Player at A is know at position B.

Repeat the drill and build up to a crisp series of *one* touches.

Distance = 10 metres for middle-position player B
20 metres for end player C.

Drill 16   Drills in Threes

In each of the drills the movement of the players is A to C, C to B, B to C, and so on. The distance can of course be varied and the intensity of the movement can be jog, stride or sprint.

1   Dribble the ball to the half-way mark RS then pass to end player and sprint the second half.

2   Move from P to Q, keeping the ball off the ground.

3   Dribble to half-way, turn on the ball and move backwards, bringing the ball along with the sole of the foot.

4   Player A and C set off together. A dribbles the ball to the centre-line RS and leaves the ball for player C to take to position P.

5   *Two-touch practice* Each player has two touches of the ball, one to control and one to pass, before moving across the space PQ.

6   Keep the ball up using heading only.

7   Move across the space feinting and swerving as in a dribble.

Drill 17   Continuous Defending

Player D defends for 1 minute. Players A,B and C pass the ball along the lines of the square. Passing across the square is not allowed. If player D moves to D1 then A would move to A1 to allow C to make a pass to him.

The organization is the same for players A,B and C when they defend for 1 minute. The defending player counts how many times he touches the ball.

34

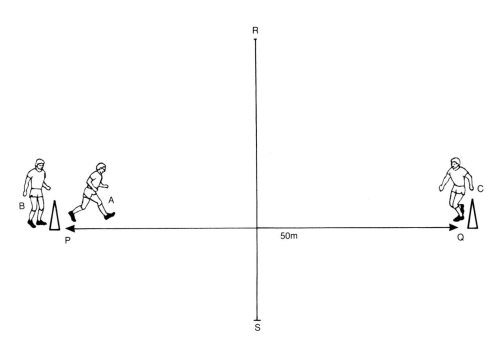

Fig 23   Drill 16.

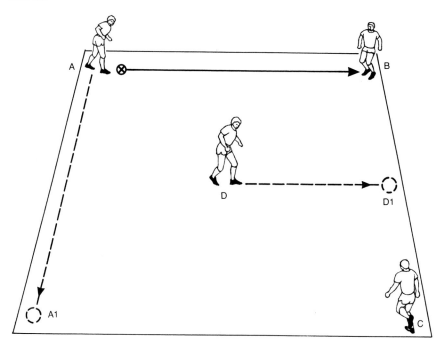

Fig 24   Drill 17.

These are just a few ideas on warming up with a ball. There are of course unlimited variations on any basic theme but the principles involved here are to use a ball at all times and to warm up over a sufficiently long period of time without involving the players in explosive muscular activities. When players have warmed up properly, they are ready to engage in stretching and flexibility exercises.

STRETCHING AND FLEXIBILITY EXERCISES

When the body has been warmed up by some vigorous introductory exercises it is necessary to stretch all the main muscle groups and to mobilize the joint complexes ready for the remainder of the training session.

Guidelines

1 Certain stretching and flexibility exercises which have been used in sports training for many years have recently been called into question. In some cases stretching exercises may have contributed to strains and stresses in muscles, tendons and joints, especially where any overload principle has been used. The following exercises are therefore suggested in the light of current thinking and should involve the player in simple self-regulated movement patterns.

2 In stretching a muscle and its associated tendons there is a point in the movement when the athlete feels he can go no further. This is the 'end position' of the range of movement associated with that particular muscle or muscle group.

3 It is strongly recommended that the player does *not* 'bounce' the limb against this end position. At the position where the muscle begins to feel pain as a result of the stretching action, the player should gently squeeze for 5–8 seconds against this end position. At no time should the pain be severe, since this may be an indication that stress or damage is being caused to muscle fibres or the tendon insertions to the bones.

Especially at non-league level, stretching and flexibility are often neglected because of lack of training time. However, this aspect of fitness is a very important part of the preparation for vigorous exercise and players should be encouraged to give it serious attention, since it can help to protect the body from injuries associated with pulls and strains. Generally speaking, soccer players are not amongst the most flexible of athletes and the strength developed in the legs (especially at the ankle and knee) tends to allow limited movement associated with the range required for powerful kicking of the ball.

A flexible joint need not be a weak joint. Strength is supplied by the muscles which operate the joint and soccer players should train to increase the range of movement at all major joints in order to be more flexible and agile in their range of movement. This is particularly true of the ankle joint. One has only to watch a male ballet dancer to see the immense power he can generate in his leaps, whilst as an athlete he is very supple in addition to being very strong. Some of the training exercises of the dancer could feature in the schedule of training for a soccer player and be of considerable benefit. After all, at the highest artistic level, soccer is very much a vigorous dance in association with a ball!

Exercise 1   Head and Neck

Note Do not do head-circling exercises. Support the head with the hands at all times, as shown in the photographs.

1 Stretch laterally, head supported by the hand, ear to shoulder, to left and right, as shown in Figs 25 and 26.

2 Tilt the head back with support from both hands (Fig 27).

3 Then press the head slowly down to the chest (Fig 28).

Figs 25 and 26   Support the head with the hand. Lateral stretch to the left and the right.

Fig 26.

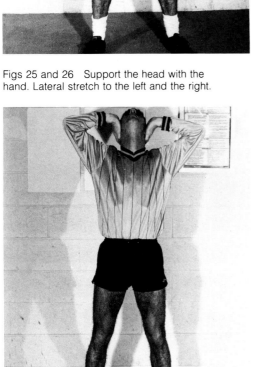

Fig 27   Tilt the head back with support from both hands.

Fig 28   Slow press down to the chest.

Exercise 2   Shoulders and Chest

1   Stretch the shoulders by tucking the head between the knees, grasp the ankles and make the back as round as possible (Fig 29).
2   With hands on ears, bring alternate knees to the forehead (Fig 30).
3   Stretch the chest by squeezing the shoulders back as far as possible and throw the chest forward (Fig 31).
4   Stretch by rising up on the elbows and forearms as far as possible with head level with the body (Figs 32 and 33).

Fig 29   Stretch the shoulders by tucking the head between the knees, grasp the ankles and make the back as round as possible.

Fig 30   Hands on ears, bring alternate knees to the forehead.

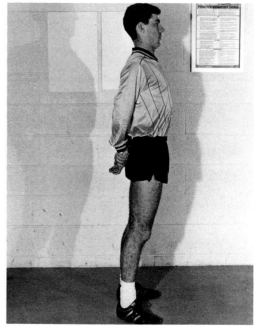

Fig 31   Stretch the chest by squeezing the shoulders back as far as possible and throw the chest forward.

Fig 32   Starting position for stretching the chest.

Fig 33   Stretch by rising up on the elbows and forearms as far as possible with the head in line with the body.

Exercise 3   Trunk

1   Rotate trunk and hips. Start as in Fig 34, with arms at right angles to the body. Finish as in Fig 35. Put the left foot into the right hand with arms at right angles to the ground and shoulders on the floor all the time. Then put the right foot into the left hand.

2   Stretch the trunk laterally, starting as in Fig 36 and finishing as in Fig 37. Keep the body in line as you slide the hand down the leg as far as you can.

3   With hands on ears, rotate the trunk, starting as in Fig 38 and finishing as in Fig 39. Keep the body upright and do not move the feet.

Fig 34   Starting position for trunk and hip rotation. Arms at right angles to the body.

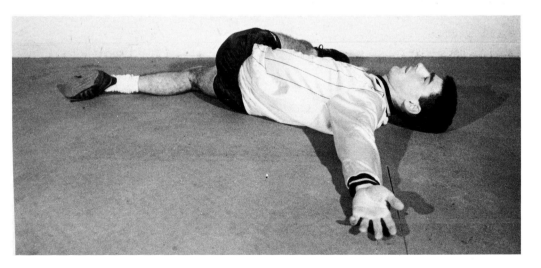

Fig 35   Finishing position for trunk and hip rotation.

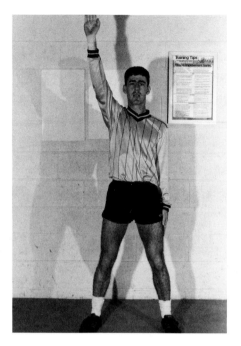

Fig 36 Starting position for the lateral stretch.

Fig 37 Finishing position for the lateral stretch.

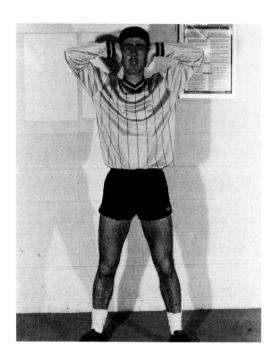

Fig 38 Starting position for trunk rotation.

Fig 39 Finishing position for trunk rotation.

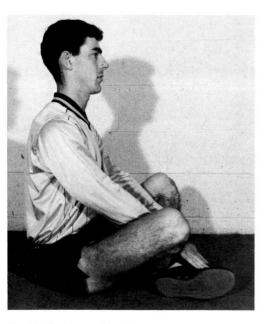

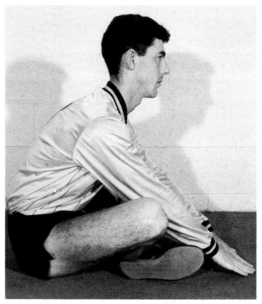

Fig 40 Starting position for lower back stretching.

Fig 41 Finishing position for lower back stretching.

Exercise 4 Back

Stretch the lower back, starting as in Fig 40, with back and head kept straight and in line. Finishing as in Fig 41. Slide the hands along the floor as far as possible but keep the head and back in one line.

2 Rock back, pulling the knees to the chest (Fig 42).

3 With hands on ears, stretch the upper back by bringing alternate knees to the chest. This is similar to the exercise shown in Fig 30, above.

Fig 42 Rock back, pulling the knees to the chest.

Exercise 5   Abdomen

Lying on a towel or a ball, push up with the
arms and lift the chest. Keep the head and
back in one line (Figs 43 and 44).

Fig 43   Lying on a rolled towel or a ball.

Fig 44   Push up with the arms and lift the chest.

Exercise 6
Front Thigh Muscles (Quads)

Lying on your front, grasp the foot and pull it in towards the buttock (Fig 45). Alternatively, with a hand on a wall (or leaning on a partner) pull the right leg to the buttock with left hand and vice versa (Fig 46).

Hamstring Muscles (Back of Thigh)

1 Keeping the front leg straight, squeeze forward and down towards the lower shin and foot (Fig 47).
2 With the front leg straight, squeeze forwards and press the body towards the ground (Fig 48).

Fig 45   Stretching the quads in a lying position.

Fig 46   Stretching the quads supported by wall.

Fig 47   Squeezing towards the lower shin and foot.

Fig 48   Squeezing forwards and pressing the body towards the ground.

43

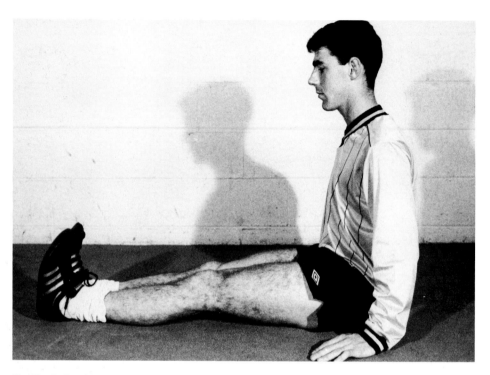

Fig 49   Pulling the toes towards the body.

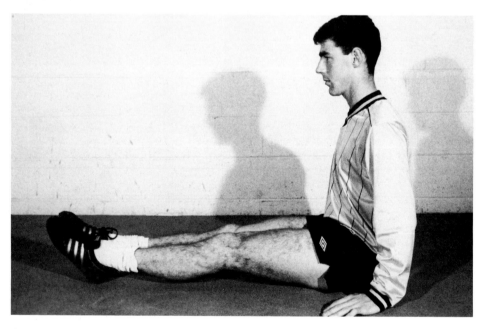

Fig 50   Pushing the toes away from the body.

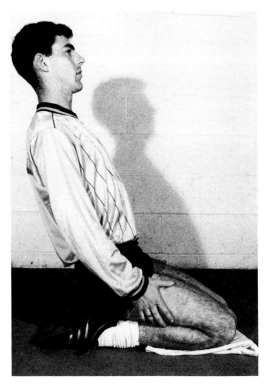

Fig 51   Squeezing down on the insteps.

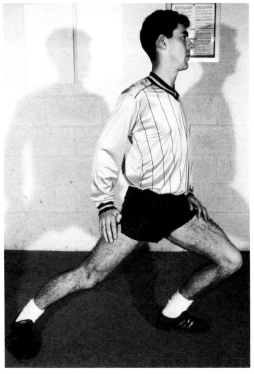

Fig 52   Stretching the calf muscle.

Exercise 7   Lower Leg and Ankle

1   In a sitting position, with legs straight, stretch the shin and calf muscles by pulling the toes towards the body and pushing them away from the body (Figs 49 and 50).
2   Stretch the shin muscles by sitting on the heels and squeezing down on the insteps with the toes pointed (Fig 51).
3   To stretch the calf muscles, while on the front foot push the knee beyond the vertical with the toes and squeeze forwards, keeping the heel of the foot on the ground (Fig 52).

Exercise 8   Groin

Starting with the leg out to the side, kneeling on other knee, raise the leg to the horizontal and squeeze (Figs 53 and 54).
2   Start with legs wide astride, arms up, back straight (Fig 55). Keeping the back straight, lean as far forward as you can (Fig 56).
3   With the back leg straight and in line with body and head, support the body with the arms and squeeze down on the groin region (Fig 57).
4   With one leg out to the side and straight, and the body upright, squeeze down towards the ground behind the other heel (Fig 58).

A simple stretching exercise has been given for each main muscle and joint, but there are many more. For further information on stretching and flexibility exercises, see the Bibliography.

45

Fig 53 Starting position for groin stretch.

Fig 54 Raise the leg to the horizontal position and squeeze.

Fig 55   Starting position with legs wide astride, arms up and back straight.

Fig 56   Finishing position. Lean as far forward as you can but keep the back straight.

Fig 57   Squeezing down on the groin region.

Fig 58   Squeezing down towards the ground behind the other heel.

STRENGTH TRAINING

In order to improve the strength of muscles work must be done against a resistance. It is possible to use one's own body weight in certain instances, for example in running up a steep hill, but generally one thinks of weight training when considering resistance training. The following exercises aim to strengthen certain muscles for the soccer player. They use either fixed-apparatus weights or the weight of the player's body.

Sets of 10 exercises should be possible in each case without too much strain. In each exercise, the first picture is the starting position and the second picture is the finishing position.

Fixed Apparatus Work

See Figs 59–74.

Figs 59 and 60   Exercise 9   Front thigh muscles (quadriceps).

Fig 60.

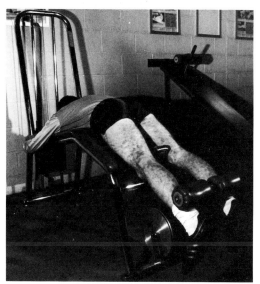

Figs 61 and 62   Exercise 10   Hamstring muscles.

Fig 62.

Figs 63 and 64   Exercise 11   Back muscles.   Fig 64.

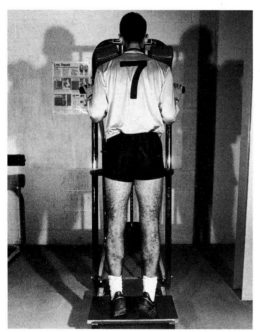
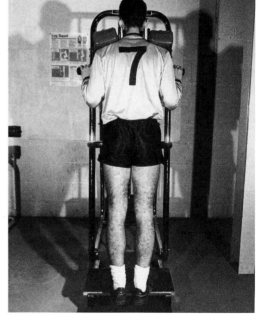

Figs 65 and 66   Exercise 12   Calf and ankle muscles. Fig 66   Note that there is no need to go on to tip-toes.

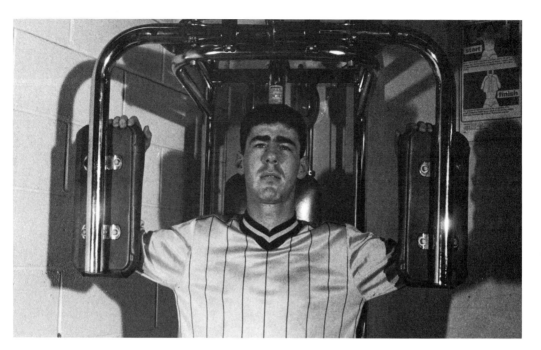

Figs 67 and 68   Exercise 13   Chest muscles.

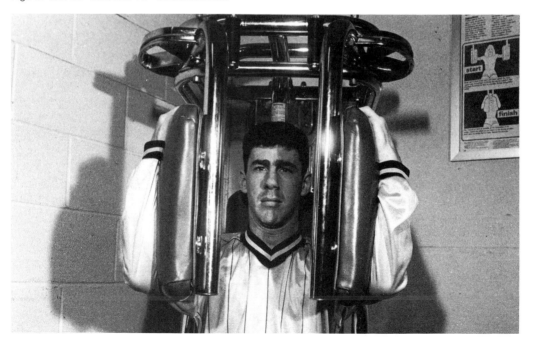

Fig 68.

51

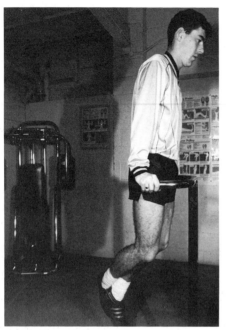

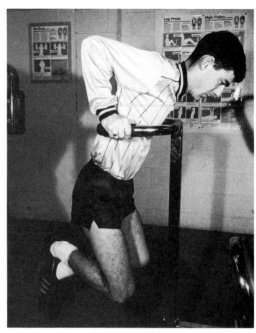

Figs 69 and 70 Exercise 14 Arm muscles
(triceps).

Fig 70.

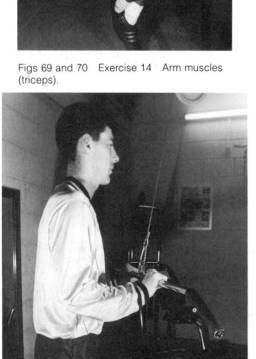

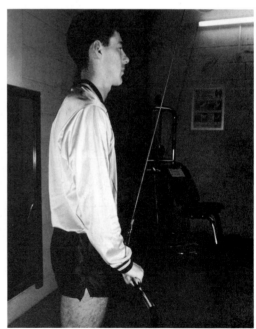

Fig 71 Alternate exercise for triceps.

Fig 72.

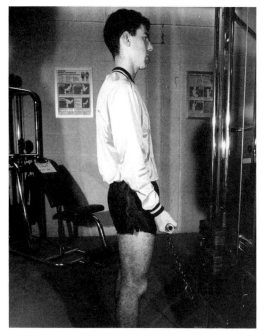 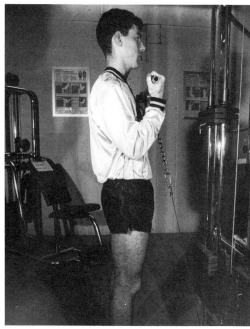

Figs 73 and 74   Exercise 15   Arm muscles (biceps).   Fig 74.

Player's Own Body Weight

Fig 75   Exercise 16   Press-ups (for arms and chest). Finishing position.

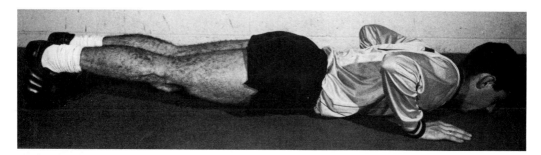

Figs 76 and 77   Exercise 17   Press-ups (mainly for arm strength).

Fig 77.

Fig 78   Exercise 18   Press-ups can be made harder by raising the legs with the feet on a bench.

Exercise 19   Abdominal (Stomach) Muscles

The starting position for sit-ups should be with the hands on the shoulders across the chest, as in Fig 79. Bend the knees as you sit up (Fig 80). The knees should still be bent in the finishing position.

The difficulty can be increased by placing the hands on the ears (Fig 81) or, alternatively, holding the hands above the head (Fig 82).

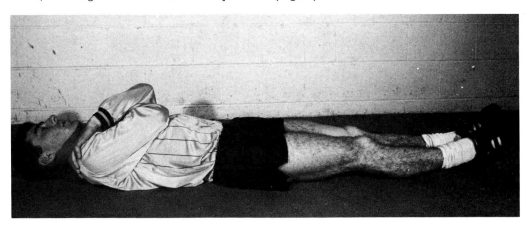

Fig 79   Starting position for sit-up.

Fig 80   Finishing position for sit-up, with the knees bent.

Fig 81 Increase the difficulty for the sit-up by placing the hands on the ears.

Fig 82 Increase the difficulty even more by holding the arms straight up above the head.

Fig 83 The step-up position for leg strengthening. The player steps on and off the bench keeping the body straight.

Exercise 20 Leg Muscles

Step up on and off a bench as shown in Fig 83. Keep the back straight.
Note A programme would normally consist of three sets of each exercise.

It must be stressed that where weights are used exercises should be carefully supervised and the correct technique should be taught by a specialist. Where there is any doubt, a very light weight should be used and the number of repetitions increased. There should not be any exercises which demand slow, painful lifts with large weights.

DIET

Although diet is an important element in fitness, this book will not go into great detail. A detailed account can be found in the chapter on Healthy Eating in *Get Ready for Soccer*[10] and only a few common-sense points will be made at this stage. A normal healthy diet is permissible for all sports people and the important issue is how close to the game food or liquid should be taken.

It is generally accepted that three hours is the safe interval one should allow between the last main meal and a game of soccer. The body shunts blood to the digestive system while we digest a meal and if we then call on the blood supply to work the muscles in a game of soccer the body will divert the blood from the digestive tract and indigestion will follow. This can cause considerable discomfort or pain and will almost certainly cause a drop in performance.

Many players will have taken food or liquid within the three-hour period and will claim that it had no detrimental effect upon their game, but this point is very debatable. Most certainly a meal involving meat and vegetables should be three hours away from a serious game of soccer.

It should not be necessary to supplement a normal healthy diet with extra vitamins but during the winter it has been shown that added amounts of vitamins can help in combating the seasonal occurrence of colds and influenza, and a lack of sunlight on the body.

During the day before a match it is beneficial to bias the diet in favour of carbohydrates. This will make sure that the supply of sugars within the muscles and liver is topped up. Beyond these few aspects of diet, the whole issue of food intake is very much a matter of common sense and for the top-class performers in any sport a wealth of literature is available, most certainly in relation to energy requirements.

SUMMARY

Fitness has a special relationship with skill. All the elements of speed, stamina, strength, power and flexibility are necessary in various combinations for the player to be skilful. They allow a player to carry out the techniques of the game as he makes decisions on a moment-to-moment basis. When his fitness deteriorates, there is a noticeable drop in the level of his skill.

There is a fine balance between playing, training and resting and this needs to be considered carefully to avoid the symptoms of overtraining. A good healthy diet should be adequate for the energy demands of the soccer player and it is recommended that the last full meal should be three hours before participating in the game.

When all physiological factors have been considered and the player prepared to the highest level of fitness, then it is suggested that the psychological domain becomes the final aspect which ultimately governs the level of the individual performance within the team. We shall consider the psychological influences in Chapter 6.

5 Fitness for Goalkeepers

The goalkeeper is not involved in the same workload as the outfield players but his type of fitness involves similar factors with some additional special qualities (see Appendix IV). In terms of speed, strength, power and flexibility, the goalkeeper has similar needs to all other players but it is in the area of agility and all-round body development that he has special requirements unique to his position.

He certainly needs to develop upper body strength because of the nature of his role in the team. Coupled with the demand for extra agility work is the need to sharpen his reaction time, or reflexes, so that he can respond quickly to the decisions he makes.

The goalkeeper is seldom exhausted in the physical sense, although he will tell you that he is mentally exhausted. The demands of mental application and concentration are considerable but from an aerobic and stamina point of view his requirements are much lower than those of outfield players.

What the goalkeeper does require above all is the strength, power, flexibility and agility to be able to react very quickly to game situations. This is the explosive power associated with anaerobic fitness.

The goalkeeper can participate in warm-up and stretching exercises with all other players. He can use his hands whenever appropriate in the practices. After the warm-up and mobilizing session, it is normal to work goalkeepers as a separate group, under the supervision of a coach.

Goalkeepers are specialists and, once given a training schedule, often work together unsupervised. What is important, however, is to keep the service realistic in the practices and not to allow any sloppiness to creep into the session.

A Suggested Training Schedule for a Goalkeeper

1　Warm up (20 minutes ball work)
2　Stretching exercises (20 minutes)
3　Speed work (sprinting to receive a ball and recover) (15 minutes)
4　Throwing activities (10 minutes)
5　Jumping to catch or punch (10 minutes)
6　Shot stopping and diving (15 minutes)
7　Agilities (20 minutes)
8　Kicking to target areas (15 minutes)
9　Final stretching and flexibility work (10 minutes)
　　Total　135 minutes

It is obvious that the suggested training schedule cannot be covered in each session and several of the practices can be combined (for example, speed work to retrieve a ball can be combined with throwing to a target). On occasions the goalkeeper will need to work more on certain weaknesses and of course time will also be needed for end-of-session games. However, it is easy to waste a goalkeeper's training time, especially in some final games, and occasionally it is good practice to work them on a variety of techniques and skills for an uninterrupted period of time.

SUGGESTIONS FOR ASPECTS OF THE TRAINING SCHEDULE FOR GOALKEEPERS

Warm-Up

All the practices in Chapter 4 are appropriate, but should be adapted to include handling the ball while the outfield players are heading or kicking the ball.

Stretching Exercises

The exercises listed in Chapter 4 are appropriate for goalkeepers. After stretching, the following mobilizing and limbering practices can be added.

1 Stand (Figs 84 and 85) or sit (Figs 86 and 87) back to back and pass the ball to each other with each rotation of the upper body.
2 Over-and-under practice. Pass the ball between the feet and return it over the head (Figs 88 and 89).
3 Lying on the floor back to back, pass the ball over the head, gripping it with the feet (Figs 90, 91 and 92).
4 Forward roll holding the ball (Figs 93, 94 and 95).
5 Backward roll holding the ball (Figs 96, 97 and 98).

Figs 84 and 85 Trunk twisting in the standing position.

Fig 85.

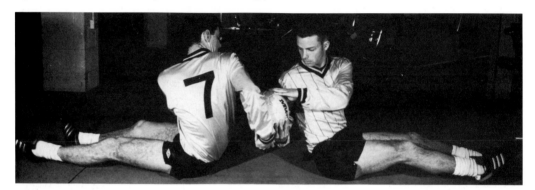

Figs 86 and 87 Trunk twisting exercise in the sitting position.

Fig 87.

Figs 88 and 89 Over-and-under practice.

Fig 89.

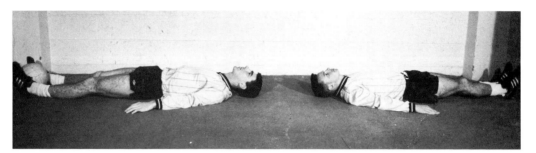

Fig 90   Passing the ball with the feet. Starting position.

Fig 91   Transferring the ball between the player's feet.

Fig 92   The feet being lowered to the floor to complete the exercise.

Fig 93   Forward roll holding the ball. Starting position.

Fig 94   The forward roll over the right shoulder.

Fig 95   Finishing position.

Fig 96   Backward roll holding the ball. Starting position.

Fig 97   The backward roll over the right shoulder.

Fig 98   Finishing position.

DRILLS FOR GOALKEEPERS

Drill 18 Speed Work for Two Goalkeepers

Starting from the middle of the goal, under the crossbar, goalkeeper A sprints to gather a ball served into the penalty area from player at B. After collecting the ball he throws a return to B and jogs back to the middle of the goal-line under the crossbar.

This drill is repeated five times and then the goalkeepers must change round so that each has a turn.

The service can also be made from points B1 or B2.

Distance sprinted = approximately 15–18
metres
Repetitions × 5 = 75–90 metres

Drill 19 Throwing Activities combined with Jumping to Catch or Punch

Goalkeeper A starts off on the goal-line in the middle of the goal. The service from B or B1 is from hands or feet but it has to be a high service, aimed between the penalty spot and the six-yard line. Goalkeeper A collects the ball as high as possible with a one-footed take-off. As soon as he lands he throws the ball to the player at C or D in the target areas which are shaded. He can also punch the ball towards the target areas.

Drill 20 Shot Stopping and Diving

Goalkeeper A starts off in the middle of the goal under the crossbar. Player B serves ten balls in rapid succession – either hard from

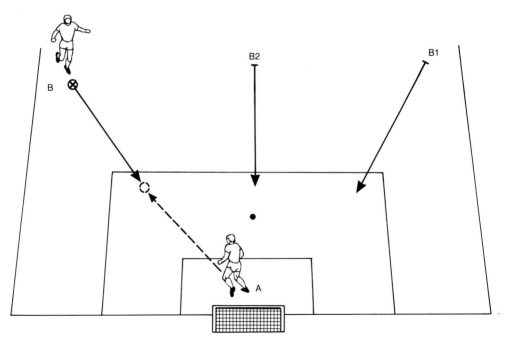

Fig 99 Drill 18.

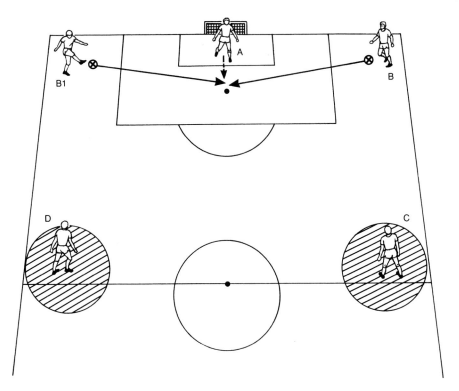

Fig 100   Drill 19.

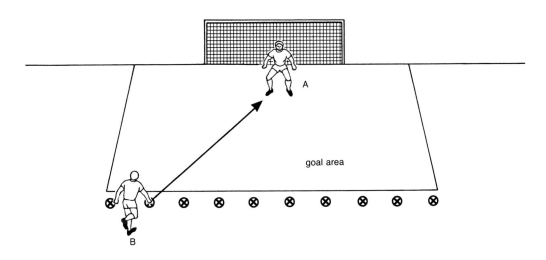

Fig 101   Drill 20.

shots or from throws to the higher parts of the goal. Each ball is served just as the goal-keeper is getting to his feet from the previous service.

Change over roles and repeat five times.

AGILITY EXERCISES

1   Bunny-hopping – bounding along taking the weight on the hands (Fig 102).
2   Dive forward roll – best done over a cane held at various heights (Fig 103) or holding the ball (Fig 104).
3   Backward roll and backward roll to hand-stand (Figs 105, 106, 107 and 108).
4   Cartwheel (Fig 109).

5   Double knee lift jumps – jump as high as possible and bring the knees up to the chest each time (Fig 110). Try doing this in sets of ten.
6   Handstand to forward roll (Figs 111 and 112).
7   Dive to reach the post. Start by positioning yourself in readiness between the cones (Fig 113). Push with power as you dive (Fig 114). You must reach the post at the end of your dive (Fig 115). This practice must be performed on very soft turf, or on gymnastic mats, or in a sand pit.
8   Kneel to reach. From a kneeling position the ball is served to the left or right and the goalkeeper has to lunge and reach to get the ball (Figs 116 and 117).

Fig 102   Taking the weight on the hands in bunny-hopping.

Fig 103   Dive forward roll over cane.

Fig 104   Dive forward roll holding a football.

67

Fig 105   Backward roll to handstand. Starting position.

Figs 106, 107 and 108   Stages of the backward roll finishing in the handstand.

Fig 107.

Fig 108.

Fig 109   The goalkeeper taking the weight on his hands in a cartwheel.

Fig 110   Double knee lift jumps.

Fig 111   The position in the handstand.

Fig 112   Finishing position after the forward roll.

Fig 113 Dive to reach the post. Starting position – perhaps between two cones for an indoor session.

Fig 114 Diving to the right. Push with power in order to reach the post.

Fig 115 The final position in the dive. Note that the left arm stays out of the way so that the keeper's vision is not obstructed.

Fig 116   Kneel to reach. Starting position with the keeper in the kneeling position.

Fig 117   Finishing position after pushing off from the kneeling position to gather the ball.

71

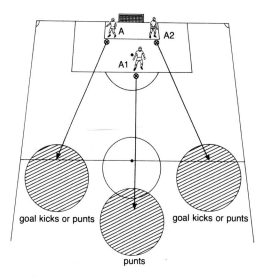

Fig 118   Drill 21.

Fig 119   Drill 22.

The above agilities help to develop power on take-off and the ability to land when taking the weight on the hands or feet. A goalkeeper must be prepared to dive or jump anywhere at any time during the game and these practices will help to keep him agile.

Drill 21   Kicking to Target Areas

As with the techniques of throwing, the goalkeeper should also develop accuracy with his kicking. He should aim for target areas with his punt kicks from his hands and also with the goal kicks.

12 kicks from each side for goal kicks at A and A2.

24 kicks from hands at Al.

Drill 22   Special Combination Practices for Goalkeepers

Goalkeeper A is put under pressure for a given period of time with services from six players. When he retrieves the ball he must throw or punt the ball to the target areas shaded.

The services are: high crosses from S1 and S4; shots or throws to all areas of the goal from S2 and S3; and balls rolled into the penalty area from S5 and S6 for the goalkeeper to sprint out to retrieve them.

This practice obviously needs lots of footballs but if each server starts with two the goalkeeper should get a short rest while the footballs are retrieved. He could also roll some footballs which he collects to servers, as well as hitting the target areas.

The coach can call each service in turn as he requires, together with the response which the goalkeeper must make – for example: kick to target; throw to target; throw to server; and so on.

Note

There is no point in working a goalkeeper to exhaustion if you require skill or technique in the practice. In the actual game he is seldom, if ever, near to fatigue levels. Further reading for goalkeeping fitness and technique is suggested in the Bibliography.

6   Mental Fitness

There is very little which can be stated with certainty when we consider the psychological factors involved in performance but there is enough information in the literature[11] to suggest that certain aspects of mental events can either enhance or cause a fall in physical performance.

PERSONALITY

All studies which try to explain why one person behaves differently from another in the same situation are studies of aspects of personality. People differ in the way in which they respond to a specific event and seldom, if ever, do they approach a similar event in the same frame of mind on another occasion. This is due to the individual nature of all facets of our personality. Within a team the problem is complicated by the obvious fact that each player will approach a situation from a slightly different point of view.

Players are either more or less extrovert and more or less neurotic in their make-up. They also respond to situations with more or less anxiety and the problem is further complicated by a host of other factors, such as the importance of the game and the worries that the player brings from influences outside the game of soccer.

STRESS

All these influences can be looked upon as stress. We can construct a framework in which the game and all its variables (training, injury, interpersonal relationships and the like) can be viewed as methods of coping with these stresses. Both individually and collectively, the manager, coaching staff and all the players have to come to terms with all the various forms of stress so that each individual can produce the best performance for each game. This is very difficult to achieve and seldom is it possible to say that every player reached his optimum performance in the same game. It is a matter of 'getting it all together', and everyone involved in sport will know what this means and the feelings it brings when it happens.

Some possible sources of stress and the effect that these stresses can exert on the player's mental approach to the game are illustrated in Fig 120.

As an example, let us consider the crowd factor shown in Fig 120. A section of the spectators continually barracks and harasses a particular player during home games. We know that this kind of treatment becomes very stressful and eventually the player may ask for a transfer from the club. This form of stress, like many others, requires that a player should construct positive mental approaches to the problem, so that he adopts coping strategies for stress factors. If he cannot do this, game performance will suffer.

In this aspect of preparation, the coaches and the managers have a big responsibility, because they often set demanding levels of expectation for the players. They need to know the various stress factors involved with each player if they are to get the best from the team effort. Whilst it is recognized that within a club it is not possible for a coach or manager to know every stress being experienced by every player, it is nevertheless safe to say that this psychological preparation is a vital factor in team performance. The greater the knowledge a coach or manager has of the personality of all of his players, the

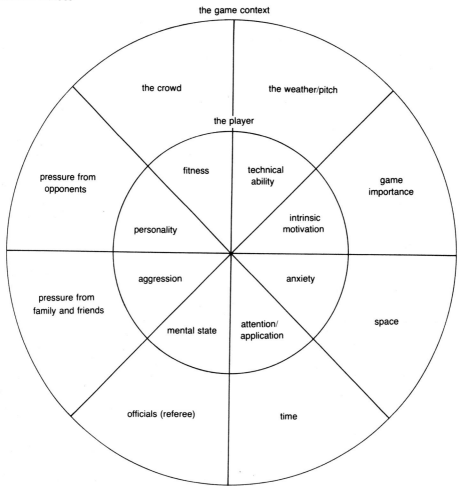

Fig 120 Stress and the soccer player.

more likely he is to be able to help them cope with the various game stresses and to motivate them to a high level of performance.

MENTAL FACTORS

The influences of mental preparation upon performance falls into three broad categories: the mental approach to each game (motivation and arousal), mental rehearsal, and the attention demands of performance.

The Mental Approach to Each Game – Motivation and Arousal

It is generally accepted that unless a player is motivated to play his performance will suffer. This is true of training as well as of actual match play. The physiological state of arousal is closely associated with being motivated and an alert, attentive and interested player is more likely to produce a good performance than an uninterested and easily distracted player.

When a player is motivated and physiologically aroused, we often say that he is 'psyched up'. The adrenalin is flowing within the body, and it seems that we can never be certain about the limits of human performance when a person is truly motivated and highly aroused.

What we do know, however, is that the level of arousal necessary to produce the best performance varies from person to person. Too little or too much arousal means that performance is below its best. This was the finding of studies[12] which became known as the inverted-U hypothesis. Although it is purely theoretical in nature, we can see that it has more than a grain of truth when applied to games such as soccer (see Fig 121). At point X the player is not aroused sufficiently and at point Y the player is over-aroused. Both points suggest that performance suffers. At point Z the optimum level is reached and this is the best level of arousal for that occasion.

At a common-sense level, all coaches and managers know when a player is not motivated sufficiently and all students of the game will know the effects of being over-aroused. This latter condition is seen in very tense and important games, where players are highly charged psychologically and for the first fifteen or twenty minutes of the game the ball is often 'ill treated', as players struggle to gain a rhythm and control of the ball. No one person seems capable of coping with the pressure within the game and the stress of 'no-risk' playing is evidenced by a lack of control and continuity. After a while, the game often settles down and this corresponds to a lowering of levels of arousal for some players. It is then that the flow of passes and confidence to keep possession may develop. This development is always very much appreciated by the spectators.

A simple equation[13] can be used to show the importance of motivation in relation to physical performance and it states that:

PERFORMANCE = SKILL × MOTIVATION

This of course is very theoretical and cannot be quantified but it suggests that performance at any time is dependent upon the factors of skill and motivation.

It can be used to explain the occasional upset in the FA Cup, where the First Division team is beaten by the non-league side. On the day, it would be expected that the superior skill of the First Division team would be the deciding factor but the higher motivation of the non-league team has the effect of nullifying the skill of the First Division players. We are all familiar with results such as this and they happen quite regularly in cup competitions. It is not suggested that the underdogs do not display good levels of skill in their play but it does point to the vital part that motivation plays in performance in a game such as soccer.

Motivation, therefore, is a very important element in playing soccer. It can be of either an extrinsic or an intrinsic nature.

Extrinsic Motivation

Extrinsic motivation is thought of as coming from outside the player and we associate this with the input from a coach, a manager or the crowd. It includes rewards and bonuses and any factors which help to urge the player to greater efforts.

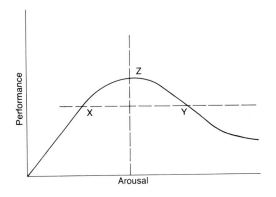

Fig 121   Inverted-U hypothesis.

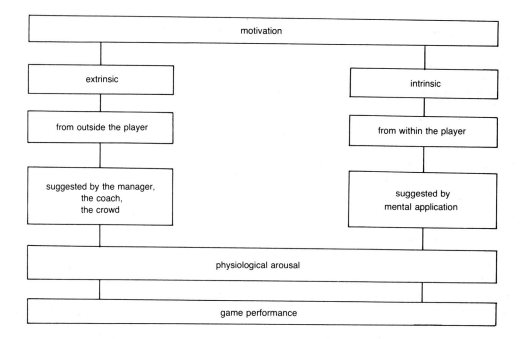

Fig 122 The relationship between motivation, arousal and performance.

Intrinsic Motivation

Intrinsic motivation is the driving force which comes from within the player and ultimately this is the crucial aspect of being motivated. Many players can be relied upon to give of their best whenever they play soccer. They play for pride of performance as well as for any external rewards. They are the backbone of any team.

Other players perform spasmodically and do not seem able to motivate themselves for some ordinary league matches. They may be excellent on the big occasion but quite often they need external motivation from the manager or coach in order to achieve a good performance.

Herein lies the problem for the manager or coach. Part of his responsibility is to motivate the team to achieve its best performance but within the team there will be players who need extra motivation, whilst others are well motivated intrinsically and do not require any further arousal, which might diminish their level of performance. This dilemma can never truly be resolved but a detailed knowledge of each player, built up over time, will allow the coach or manager to make the best assessment of who needs to be aroused and who needs to be kept cool during team preparations and pre-match talks.

Intrinsic motivation should be tapped more often. Where a player is confident, fit and free from stress, he should be able to concentrate and prepare himself mentally for the forthcoming game. We can see that this mental state makes certain assumptions but where a player is inwardly happy with his fitness, his level of skill, his role within the team and his responsibilities and priorities in relation to the tactics and strategies outlined for the team, he should be able to tune himself mentally and thereby intrinsically motivate himself for the game ahead.

This aspect of preparation brings in the notion of mental rehearsal, which, in the final minutes before a player goes out to play, can act as a trigger for intrinsic motivation.

Mental Rehearsal

It is difficult and often unwise to attempt to apply psychological theories to the practical setting of sport, because there are so many unpredictable factors involved. Although the whole question of cause and effect is centred in uncertainty, literary evidence[14] and common sense show that mental rehearsal can help to improve performance.

It involves the player in thinking through the various techniques and skills which he will use during the game, or rehearsing the basic team tactics and strategies which have been decided during preparations for the match. This mental technique is probably best used in the final minutes before a player goes out to play and a few examples will show the principles involved.

Mental Rehearsal for a Goalkeeper

'See' the ball coming from the wing into your goal area. 'See' yourself jumping to catch the ball. 'Feel' the technique in your hands as you spread your fingers and thumbs to cradle the ball. 'See' yourself land and tuck the ball into your body. There are numerous pictures that the goalkeeper can rehearse as he prepares for the game and in all the scenes he should 'see' himself being successful. He should 'see' and 'feel' good footwork and staying well balanced, ready to make decisions about stopping shots, leaving his line, narrowing angles, or going out to a forward's feet.

Mental Rehearsal for an Outfield Player

'See' and 'feel' yourself executing good footwork. 'See' the ball coming towards you.

Where are the opponents? (This picture will be in relation to the position the player occupies in the team). Where is the pressure coming from? What will you do? Where will you go? Which space will be yours?

Tell yourself you can answer the problem and do it over and over again. 'See' yourself being successful.

Mental Rehearsal for All Team Players regarding Team Strategies

When playing two strikers, a well-known ploy is to play the ball to the front men as early as possible and, from the subsequent possession, support with wide players and midfield players who will go forward into attack (see Fig 123). This 'team shape' can be mentally rehearsed, so that players are looking for that picture in the actual game, which helps them with decision making. In a way, it is pre-programming a decision but the player will always have to assess the actual game picture to see if the pass is possible or not.

Mental Rehearsal for Switching Play from One Side of the Pitch to the Other

When observing a soccer match it is noticeable how often 20 players occupy quite small areas of the field. In team practice and preparation it is obviously necessary that players, especially in midfield and defence, should be aware of the shape and movement of the total game picture and switch the play accordingly. This can be mentally rehearsed before the players go onto the field. See Fig 124.

Summary

The coach or manager will have many more pictures which he wishes the players to 'see' in the moments before they go out to play (for example, corners, throw-ins, free kicks) and

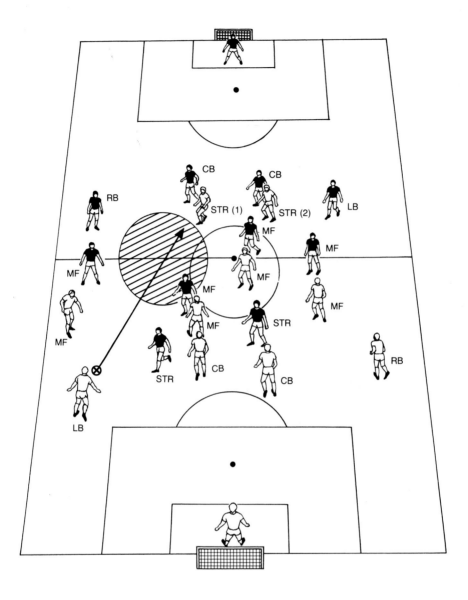

Fig 123   Mental rehearsal – passing forward. White left back (LB) has possession. The space to pass to in relation to the striker (STR(1)) is the shaded area.

it is important that players should mentally tune themselves to 'see' these in action as a 'mental set' before they leave the dressing-room. Where, for instance, three players are involved in a special free kick just outside the opponents' penalty area, it is vital that they mentally rehearse this in the dressing-room, to make sure that they all know what their role is in the action. They will only get one chance on the pitch! Mentally rehearsing

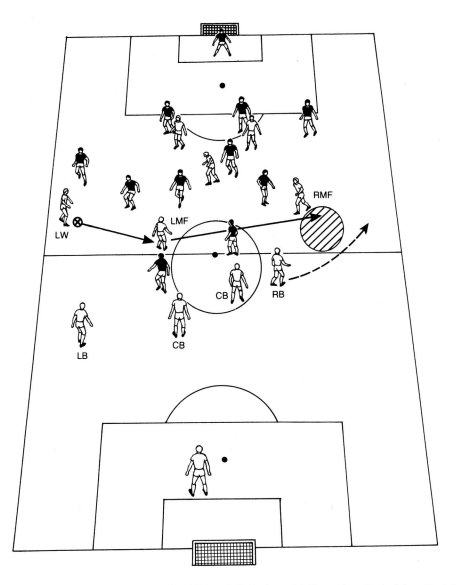

Fig 124 Mental rehearsal – switching play. White midfield player (LMF) receives the ball from the left winger (LW). It would now be a sound move to switch the play to the shaded zone where (RMF) could receive the ball and (RB) could support him.

game pictures also aids in motivating the player intrinsically and bringing his total attention and concentration upon the game.

Mental aspects of preparation are very important components for any sports person and in a team they are particularly crucial. Only when a team can think similar thoughts during each moment of a game can it claim to be a team. Without this knowledge and understanding of the various roles of individuals within the overall team plan, and a clear idea of their own priorities and responsibilities to the team, each player will tend to act as a separate unit and the team is then made up of eleven isolated ideas. The concept of team requires that each player has a good understanding of what the whole team is trying to achieve at any moment during a game and the part that he should play in the overall plan.

The Attention Demands of Performance

Team games such as soccer make great demands upon the players' ability to attend to what is going on. At one moment we expect players to know the whereabouts of team mates and opponents and the next moment to concentrate upon the technique of chest control, followed by a shot on goal. These demands mean that a player's attention must shift easily between a wide picture of the total game (scanning) to the narrow (focus) picture of the ball and his immediate intention.[15]

It is known that some players seem unable to hold a picture of the total game as it changes from moment to moment and play their football in areas which are quite close to them. Even with the power to pass over long distances, their play appears blinkered and their passes are mostly short – within 25–30 metres.

There seems little doubt that this wider vision can be improved by conditioned games (for example passing to the forwards whenever you have time and space) but this must be developed alongside the mental application of the player who is, after all, making changes to his decision making, perhaps in association with a required improvement in his technique, especially his first touch, and a mental set which suggests to him: 'Hit a long ball'.

It is all part of the attention demands made upon the player. To change any of his acquired habits, he will need to practise making decisions slightly earlier, in order to have enough time and space to carry out the technique. Coupled with this, the player will need to constantly carry a picture of where the forwards are during each second of the game, so that he knows where to pass the ball when he receives it.

During the game, therefore, the player's attention must take in the ever-changing position of team-mates (this is aided by communication on the pitch) and the opponents, so that he can make decisions about his intentions as quickly as possible. These decisions should ultimately be made before he receives the ball, so that decision time can be reduced. This is particularly important where the player is under severe pressure as he receives the ball. To control the ball first and then make a decision about what to do next may cost him possession. Fig 125 represents the elements of response time in diagrammatic form.

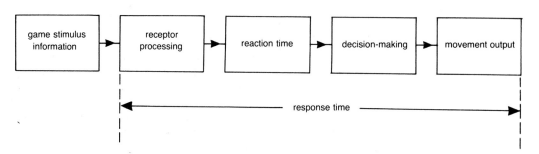

Fig 125   Elements of response time.

TIME, SPACE AND PRESSURE

Attention to the changing scene is vital for the soccer player. All his game skills take place within a framework of time, space and pressure and it is the element of pressure which ultimately finds out how good his techniques and skills really are.

Fig 125 shows that time is required for a player to receive and process the game information (receptor processing) and his reaction time is very specific to him as a player. These two elements can be practised but not reduced in time significantly. Decision time and movement time can also be practised and refined and it is these two elements which can lead to a reduction in response time.

It is clear that if players can perfect their techniques and make decisions earlier they can reduce the total response time and in this way they actually apply more pressure to the opponents, because they allow them less time to process their intentions and their movements.

ATTENTION DEMANDS OF TECHNIQUE

When a player carries out a technique (for example, control using the thigh) he needs to blot out the wider game information. Having made the decision to control the ball with his thigh, the player must isolate himself in time and space for the few milliseconds it takes him to control the ball. His attention must not shift from the ball, otherwise he may not be successful. He has also made the decision concerning the space he is going to occupy when he has controlled the ball but, from the moment he selects the decision to the moment the ball touches his thigh, he must not pay attention to anything else. This, of course, is very difficult, especially if pressurizing players

are in close attendance, but the idea of attention must be total and concentrated on the ball, otherwise the control will suffer.

In this instance, the player is required to focus his attention on a very specific aspect of the game, with all the distractions around him at the moment in which he carries out a technique, and it can be appreciated that this is a very strict discipline for every player. In coaching, we impress upon young players that they must keep their eyes on the ball and keep their head still when performing a technique. These important points of mental attention must apply during every game.

SUMMARY

The demands upon the player for his undivided attention during every moment of a soccer match are very severe. He has to keep a picture of the total field of play in his vision and update the information every second as the players move during the game. He also has to narrow his focus of attention to the ball when carrying out the game techniques of trapping, heading, shooting, and so on. These aspects of the game require strict attention, application and concentration on the part of the player, and coaches and managers will be familiar with the small lapses in attention which cause mistakes. As a defender the lapse in concentration may lead to a goal being scored against you and as a forward it may lead to a lost opportunity to win the game.

When all aspects of preparation have been fully considered, it is generally recognized that at the highest levels of competition it is often the psychological factors which ultimately decide the outcome. A self-disciplined, attentive and highly motivated player can often make a high ratio of good decisions to poor, or bad, decisions. He can also make tired legs do that little bit extra.

Appendices

I MAX V̇O₂ VALUES AND DISTANCES RUN IN 12 MINUTES BY PROFESSIONAL FOOTBALL PLAYERS

Max V̇O₂ Values (ml O₂/kg min.)

	No. in sample	Mean	Range
Attackers	5	59.2	57.2–63.1
Midfielders	2	56.1	55.1–57.1
Defenders	9	59.3	55.0–66.7
Goalkeepers	2	53.7	53.0–54.4
Total mean	18	58.4	53.0–66.7

Distances Run (in Miles) in 12 Minutes

	No. in sample	Mean	Range
Attackers	5	1.90	1.77–2.03
Midfielders	2	1.76	1.81–1.85
Defenders	9	1.95	1.85–2.02
Goalkeepers	2	1.64	1.62–1.67
Total mean	18	1.86	1.62–2.03

Source: P.B. Raven et al., 'A physiological evaluation of professional soccer players', Institute for Aerobics Research, Dallas, Texas, 1976.

II TAKING A HEART-RATE COUNT USING THE CAROTID ARTERY

1 Place two fingers across the throat and press in towards the muscle of the neck, as shown in Fig 126.
2 Find the pulse as a regular beat.
3 On the beat say 'zero' and start the stop-watch.
4 Count from zero onwards for 15 seconds, looking at the stop-watch.
5 As the watch reaches 15 seconds, stop counting, then multiply the number by 4 to get heartbeats per minute, and record this reading.

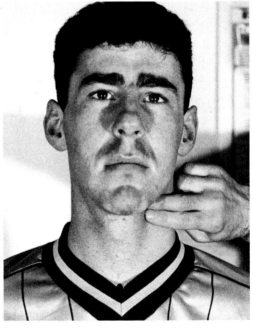

Fig 126 Position of the fingers on the neck of a player when the carotid pulse count is taken.

III THE KALAMEN 50-YARD DASH (SIMPLIFIED)

1 Player starts on line AB at X.
2 Player should be sprinting flat out as he crosses line CD.
3 As player crosses line CD person at D brings a flag down quickly to signal that he has crossed the line.
4 At this point stop-watches are started by persons C and E.

5 As player crosses line EF person at F brings down a flag and both stop-watches are stopped.
6 The stop-watch readings are taken and an average recorded.
7 The run should be repeated three times and the best reading recorded.
8 Allow the player sufficient time to recover between trials.

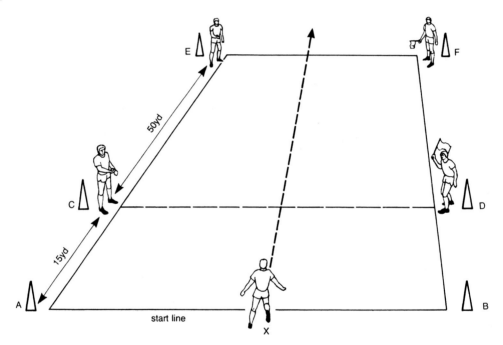

Fig 127 The Kalamen 50-yard dash (simplified).

IV MOVEMENT DISTANCES BY PLAYERS (IN METRES)

	Mean	**Range**
Walking	3,026	2,493–3,559
Jogging	5,134	3,700–6,580
Striding	1,506	922–2,090
Sprinting	666	355–977
Walking backwards	590	329–861
Jogging backwards	285	46–524
Moving sideways	316	181–451
Travel with the ball	218	117–319
Total	11,523	8,026–15,042

Number in sample = 20

Source: R.T. Withers, 'Match analysis of Australian professional soccer players', *Sports Coach*, 1978, no. 3.

IV DETAIL OF GOALKEEPER'S MOVEMENTS (IN METRES)

Jog	1,088
Walk	1,338
Cruise	497
Sprint	32
Move backwards	1,017
Total	3,972

Source: Reilly and Thomas, op. cit.

V   DISTANCES COVERED BY DIFFERENT POSITIONAL PLAYERS (IN METRES)

	Full backs	Central defenders	Midfielders	Forwards
Walking	2,843	3,083	2,674	3,503
Jogging	5,392	3,859	6,085	5,221
Striding	1,737	1,268	1,840	1,177
Sprinting	941	396	650	678
Walking backwards	428	736	466	729
Jogging backwards	256	428	264	190
Moving sideways	383	398	214	268
Travel with the ball	209	192	286	186
Total	11,980	10,169	12,194	11,766

Mean values in each case
Number in each sample = 5

Source: Withers, op. cit.

VI DISTANCES COVERED BY DIFFERENT POSITIONAL PLAYERS IN SPRINT AND TOTAL (IN METRES)

	Sprint	**Total**
Goalkeeper	32	3,972
Full back	787	8,245
Centre back	829	7,759
Midfield	1,063	9,805
Forward	1,068	8,397

Source: T. Reilly and V. Thomas, 'A motion analysis of work rate in different positional roles in professional football match play', *Journal of Human Movement Studies*, 1976, 2, pp. 87–97.

ANALYSIS OF DISTANCE COVERED BY A PLAYER DURING A MATCH

1 Having measured the length and width of the pitch in question, all other helpful measurements can be calculated from the standard pitch dimensions (goal area, penalty area, centre circle).

2 It is very helpful if there are two people to take the analysis because it is a very demanding task. It is suggested that each person collect data for 5 minutes and then rests for 5 minutes.

3 Lots of blank sheets of the pitch plan will be needed because one can be used for a maximum of approximately 2–3 minutes.

4 It will be necessary to check the stride pattern of the player under analysis if you wish to check for accuracy: check the distance of one sprinting stride in the middle of a sprint and check the distance of one jogging, striding and walking stride.

5 If you want a very general measure of the distances covered by a player, then the pencil-trace method will suffice, but for checks of accuracy you will need stride length measure for the player and, if possible, a video of his movements. With the video you can make an accurate count of actual strides.

6 The example in Appendix VII is for a right full back (RFB) who goes forward in attack and then recovers to a defending position.

VII ANALYSIS OF DISTANCE COVERED BY A PLAYER – AN EXAMPLE WORKING SHEET

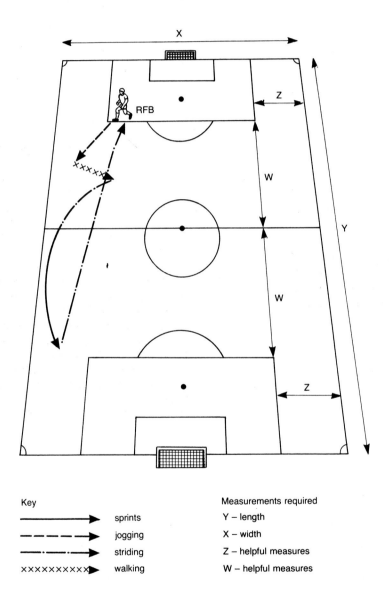

Key

—————▶ sprints

— — — —▶ jogging

—·——·—▶ striding

×××××××××▶ walking

Measurements required

Y – length

X – width

Z – helpful measures

W – helpful measures

Fig 128 Analysis of distance covered by a player. An example working sheet.

VIII PLAYER PROFILE SHEET

Name

Age   Season

Height

	End of season	Pre-season	Mid-season
Weight			
Physiological			
Resting H.R.			
5-minute run H.R.			
Max. VO$_2$			
Distance 12-minute run			
Time 50 yards dash			
5th minute aerobic (H.R. max./sub.)			

Fig 129   Player profile sheet.

IX AVERAGE MAXIMUM HEART RATE AND RECOMMENDED RANGE FOR HEART RATE DURING AEROBIC TRAINING IN HEALTHY ADULTS

From ACSM (1980)(16)

Maximum heart rate

Recommended range for heart rate during training.

Source: American College of Sports Medicine, 1980, Appendix II.

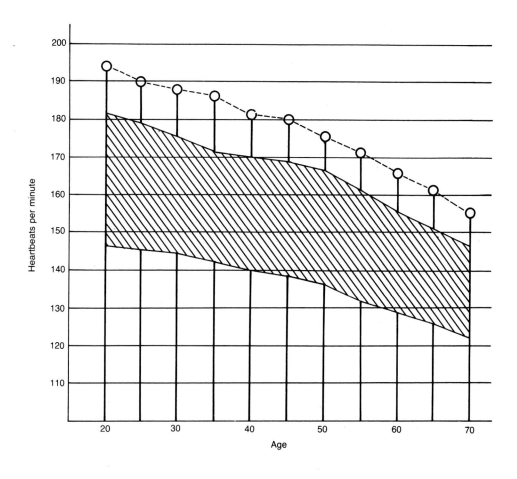

Fig 130   Average maximum heart rate and recommended range for heart rate during aerobic training in healthy adults.

Fig 131   A player being tested on a bicycle ergometer.

X MEASURING AEROBIC FITNESS USING A BICYCLE ERGOMETER

1   Take player's resting pulse rate.

2   Player warms up for 5 minutes working at 50 watts.

3   Loading increased to 150 watts.

4   Take heart rate of player after 5 minutes' work at 150 watts.

5   Decrease loading to 50 watts and recover with work for 3–5 minutes.

6   Work out the player's max VO_2 value using the formula on page 10 and check with the expected readings for fit sports people on the same page.

Glossary

Aerobic In the presence of free oxygen

Agility The flexible use of the body in motion

Anaerobic Without the presence of free oxygen

Arousal A state of physical and mental alertness

Closed season The holiday period for soccer players

CO_2 Carbon dioxide

Decision making Mental events which select the techniques and the decision to act

Drill A repeated movement sequence

Energy The capacity to do work (application of force over a distance)

Fartlek Running training which varies the speed and length of running sequences

Fast-twitch fibres White muscle fibres which produce speed

Fitness The ability of the body to do work

Flexibility The range of possible movement about a joint

Max VO_2 The maximum oxygen uptake by an athlete during intense work output

Motivation An inner driving force which compels a person to action

O_2 Oxygen

Overtraining An excess of training or match play with insufficient rest for recovery purposes

Power Work divided by time (e.g., horsepower or watts)

Practice Part of a game sequence taken in isolation

Skill The appropriate application of technique

Slow-twitch fibres Red muscle fibres which produce stamina

Speed Distance covered in a given time. (e.g., feet per second or miles per hour)

Stamina The ability to maintain work output

Strength The force which a muscle can exert against a resistance

Stress Physical or mental conditions which can cause a deterioration in performance

Technique The unique movement characteristics of a sport or activity

Work Force applied over a distance (e.g., foot-pounds (ft lb) or kilogram-centimetres (kg cm))

References

1 Fox, E. L., and Mathews, D. K., *The Physio-logical Basis of Physical Education and Athletics* (Philadelphia, Holt-Saunders, 1981), pp. 628–9.
2 ibid.
3 ibid., pp. 621–3.
4 Astrand, P. O., and Kodahl, K., *Textbook of Work Physiology*, 3rd edn. (McGraw Hill, 1986).
5 ibid.
6 Fox and Mathews, op. cit., ch. 13.
7 ibid., ch. 3.
8 Butterworth, A., 'An investigation into the demands upon professional footballers with special reference to overtraining', unpublished BA Hons dissertation, Human Movement Studies, Carnegie Department, Leeds Polytechnic, 1987.
9 Ekblom, B., 'The physiological demands of soccer, in Astrand and Kodahl, op. cit.
10 De Looy, A. 'Healthy Eating', in *Get Ready for Soccer* (Crowood, 1990).
11 Schmidt, R. A., 'Motor Control and Learning', *Human Kinetics*, 1982.
12 Yerkes, R. M., and Dodson, J. D., 'The relation of strength of stimulus to rapidity of habit-formation', *Journal of Comparative Neurological Psychology,* 18 (1908), pp. 459–82.
13 Gagne, R. M., and Fleishman, E. A., *Psychology and Human Performance* (Holt, Rinehart & Winston, 1959).
14 Schmidt, op. cit.
15 Bruner, J. S., et al., *A study of thinking* (New York, Wiley, 1965).
16 *American College of Sports Medicine,* 1980, Appendix II.
17 (i) Ekblom, B., 'Applied Physiology of Soccer', *Sports Medicine* 3, 1986 pp.50–60; (ii) Reilly, T., and Thomas, V., 'A motion analysis of work rate in different positional roles in professional football match play', *Journal of Human Movement Studies*, 1976, 2, pp. 87–97; (iii) Saltin, B., 'Metabolic fundamentals in exercise', *Medicine and Science in Sports*, 1973, 5, pp. 137–46; (iv) Vinnai, G., *Football Mania* (London, Ocean Books, 1973); (v) Wade, A., *The F.A. Guide to Training and Coaching,* (Heinemann, 1967), p. 125; (vi) Whitehead, N. J., *et al.,* 'A pilot study of the workloads of soccer players, unpublished Carnegie project, Leeds, 1968; (vii) Winterbottom, W., *Soccer Coaching* (Naldrett Press, 1959), pp. 239–41; (viii) Withers, R. T., 'Match analysis of Australian professional soccer players', *Sports Coach*, 1978, no. 3; (ix) Zelenka, V., *et al.,* 'Specific function testing of young football players', *Journal of Sports Medicine and Physical Fitness,* 1967, 7, p. 143–7.
18 Raven, B. et al., 'A physiological evaluation of professional soccer players', Institute for Aerobics Research, Dallas, Texas, 1976.

Bibliography

Cooper, K., *The Aerobics Way* (Corgi, 1978).

Donovan, G., *et al.*, *Exercise Danger* (Wellness, Australia, 1989).

Grisogono, V., *Sports Injuries – A Self-Help Guide* (John Murray, 1984).

Humphreys, J., and Holman, R., *Focus on Middle Distance Running* (Black, 1985).

Martens, R., 'Sport competition anxiety test', *Human Kinetics*, 1976.

McGrath, J. E., *A Conceptual Formulation for Research on Stress* (Holt Rinehart, 1970).

Meerloo, A., *In-Body Talk Magazine*, 1988, vol. 3.

Spielberger, C. D., 'Trait-State Anxiety and Motor Behaviour', *Journal of motor behaviour*, No. 3 (1971), p. 265–79.

Swift, J., 'The Rights and Wrongs of stretching, *Magazine of Fitness*, 1985.

Syer, J., and Connolly, C., *Sporting Body, Sporting Mind* (Cambridge University Press, 1984).

Timmermans, H. M., and Martin, M., 'Top Ten Potentially Dangerous Exercises', *JOPERD*, August 1987.

Welsh, A., *Goalkeeping* (Black, 1990).

Wilmoth, S. K., 'Leading Aerobic Dance Exercise', *Human Kinetics*, 1986.

Wilson, R., *The Art of Goalkeeping* (Pelham, 1980).

Index